This Book

Supplementary Exercises for Old Norse – Old Icelandic (a volume in the Viking Language Old Norse Series) is a workbook designed for those who want to sharpen their skills in Old Norse. It offers a wealth of Old Norse exercises along with an answer key and full vocabulary. There are also Old Norse readings drawn from the *Saga of Ragnar Lodbrok*, recounting Ragnar's attack on England and his death in the snake pit. So also passages from *The Prose Edda*, telling of a strange journey of the Norse gods and the dragon´s treasure and magical ring taken by Sigurd the Volsung.

About the Authors

JESSE BYOCK is distinguished research professor of Old Norse and Medieval Scandinavian at UCLA. He earned his Ph.D. from Harvard University and is professor at the UCLA Cotsen Institute of Archaeology, specializing in the Viking World: its sagas, history, and archaeology. In Iceland, he directs the Mosfell Archaeological Project (MAP) and teaches at the University of Iceland (Háskóli Íslands) in the Department of History and the programs of Medieval Icelandic and Viking Studies.

RANDALL GORDON is a specialist in historical linguistics of Celtic and Germanic Languages, with concentrations on the development and grammar of Old Norse and Old Irish. He received his Ph.D. in Indo-European Studies from UCLA.

www.juleswilliampress.com & www.oldnorse.org

Jules William Press publishes a range of books about the Viking Age. Its series of Old Norse primers, grammars, texts, studies, and audio pronunciation albums answer the needs of the modern student, instructor, and self-learner. The books and materials are purposely affordable and conceived with distance learning in mind. JWP also publishes a series of novels and eBooks as well as archaeological reports about the Viking period.

Supplementary Exercises for Old Norse – Old Icelandic

by

Jesse Byock and Randall Gordon

A Volume in the Viking Language Old Norse Series

www.juleswilliampress.com
www.oldnorse.org

Jules William Press

www.juleswilliampress.com
www.oldnorse.org

Supplementary Exercises for Old Norse – Old Icelandic, a volume in the Old Norse Icelandic Series

A book of supplementary exercises and original Old Norse readings to accompany *Old Norse – Old Icelandic: Concise Introduction to the Language of the Sagas* and for those who want to learn Old Norse.

Paperback ISBN: 978-0-9881764-0-9

Cover design by Basil Arnould Price.
Printed in Cambria

About These Supplementary Exercises

This book is a collection of supplementary exercises to accompany the new primer, *Old Norse – Old Icelandic: Concise Introduction to the Language of the Sagas,* which teaches how to read Icelandic sagas and Old Norse texts in the original language. The primer is divided into 17 short lessons, each opening with a passage in Old Icelandic drawn from sagas or mythological sources, and this supplementary volume has 17 lessons of additional exercises.

The supplementary exercises harmonize with the lessons in the primer. They focus on the grammar and vocabulary necessary to master the reading(s). In this way, original texts determine the instruction, and students master grammatical elements as they are needed. To speed the learning, each lesson contains a short vocabulary of new words and phrases, as well as practice exercises, reinforcing the grammatical explanations. Reading passages in the primer are drawn from the following Old Icelandic texts.

Egils saga Skalla-Grímssonar (*Egil's Saga*)
Fóstbrœðra saga (*Saga of the Foster-Brothers*)
Gísla saga Súrssonar (*Saga of Gisli Sursson*)
Gunnlaugs saga ormstungu (*Gunnlaug's Saga Serpent-Tongue*)
Hávarðar saga (*Havard's Saga*)
Heimskringla (*History of the Kings of Norway*)
Hrafnkels saga Freysgoða (*Saga of Hrafnkel the Priest of Frey*)
Landnámabók (*Sturlubók*) (*The Book of Settlements*)
Magnúss saga Erlingssonar (*Saga of Magnus Erlingsson*)
Njáls saga (*Njal's Saga*)
Óláfs saga Tryggvasonar (*Saga of Olaf Tryggvason*)
Ragnars saga loðbrókar (*Saga of Ragnar Lodbrok*)
Snorra Edda (*Snorri's Edda* [*The Prose Edda*])
Vápnfirðinga saga (*Saga of the Families of Weapon's Fjord*)
Ynglinga saga (*Saga of the Ynglings*)
Þorsteins þáttr stangarhǫggs (*The Tale of Thorstein Staff-Struck*)

This volume of *Supplementary Exercises* also includes a series of original Old Norse readings. Some are drawn from the *Saga of Ragnar Lodbrok* and recount Ragnar's attack on England and his death in the snake pit.

Others are mythological tales from *The Prose Edda*, which tell of a strange journey of the gods and events involving the treasure and magical ring taken from the dragon by Sigurd the Volsung. *Supplementary Exercises* features a complete vocabulary with all words and phrases found in the exercises and readings in the primer and is suitable for anyone learning Old Norse. A free answer key is available on our website: www.oldnorse.org.

Additional Resources

The introductory primer, *Old Norse – Old Icelandic: Concise Introduction to the Language of the Sagas*, is complemented by an **eBook** version and a series of additional texts.

***The Saga of the Families of Weapon's Fjord* (*Vápnfirðinga saga*)** is a classic Icelandic prose tale of blood feud in Viking Age Iceland. Issues of vengeance, honor, and survival dominate as two rival chieftain families struggle for power in Iceland's East Fjords. This saga edition offers a new translation and includes the original Old Norse text presented in a way that teaches how to read a complete saga in both English and Old Icelandic. The edition contains extensive notes, maps, vocabulary, and cultural explanations. The student has everything necessary to master a saga of feud, violence, and the claims of honor.

***The Tale of Thorstein Staff-Struck* (*Þorsteins þáttr stangarhǫggs*)**. This short and not-so-sweet Icelandic *þáttr* ('tale', in this instance a short saga) weighs the role of violence, while exploring insult and the duty of vengeance. *Þorsteins þáttr* captures the essence of the Icelandic sagas, but with an unusual twist. This edition offers a new English translation along with the original Old Norse text, extensive vocabulary, detailed notes, and grammar explanations. Here is a compact volume that teaches how to read sagas and to evaluate how these medieval narratives are constructed.

Table of Contents
Supplementary Exercises and Reading Passages

ACKNOWLEDGEMENTS

We thank Basil A. Price and Chad Laidlow for their thoughtful help with the exercises. Thanks also to Ilya Sverdlov for his excellent grammar comments and assistance. We also thank our editor Ashley M. Byock, who was instrumental in publishing this book.

Lesson 1 Supplementary Exercises

1. Fill in the appropriate endings.

a. Álf__ var gǫfug__ mað__. Hann var Gunnlaug__son, Bjarn___son___.

b. Ásgerð__ var móðir Þorstein__, ágæt__ mann__ ok mikil__.

2. Translate the sentences in exercise **1**.

a. ____

____

b. ____

____

3. Supply suitable personal names, nouns, and adjectives.

a. __________r var _________r um alla hluti; ___________r hét móðir ___________s ok var _________ardóttir.

b. __________r hét _________r. Hann var ___________sson, ___________s_____ar, _________s _________s ok _________s.

4. Translate your answers to exercise **3**.

a. ____

____

b. ____

____

5. The following reading comes from the introductory passage. Identify the case (nom. or gen.) of the adjectives, nouns, and personal names indicated in **bold type**.

Þorsteinn (_____) hét maðr; hann var Egilsson, Skalla-Grímssonar, Kveld-Úlfssonar, **hersis** (_____) ór Nóregi; en Ásgerðr hét móðir **Þorsteins** (_____) ok var Bjarnardóttir. Þorsteinn bjó at Borg í Borgarfirði; hann var **auðigr** (_____) at fé ok hǫfðingi mikill, **vitr** (_____) maðr ok hógværr ok hófsmaðr um alla hluti.

6. Decline the masculine nouns *konungr* 'king' and *hjálmr* 'helmet' in the singular, and the adjective *hvítr* 'white' in the masculine singular. (Hint: refere to the paradigms under section 1.2; the nouns decline like *hestr* 'horse', and the adjective declines like *góðr* 'good'.)

	Masc noun		Masc adj
Sg nom	konungr	hjálmr	hvítr
acc	________	________	________
dat	________	________	________
gen	________	________	________

7. Indicate the case of each Old Icelandic word. (Hint: refer to the paradigms under section 1.2.) Then match each word with its English meaning by drawing a line between them.

acc.	ágætan	wolf
_____	hrings	excellent
_____	úlfi	white
_____	hvítan	wealthy
_____	auðigr	ring

8. Give the case (nom., acc., or dat.) and role (subj., dir. obj., or ind. obj.) of the word in bold.

	Case	Role
a. **Ásgerðr** bjó í Danmǫrku.	________	________
b. Egill sýndi Sigurði **skip**.	________	________
c. Eiríkr gaf ('gave') **Þórólfi** hring ágætan.	________	________
d. Eiríkr sýndi **Þorsteini** hvítan úlf.	________	________
e. Álfr hét maðr; **hann** var auðigr at fé.	________	________

9. Translate the senteces in exercise **8**.

a. ________________________________

b. ________________________________

c. ________________________________

d. ________________________________

e. ________________________________

10. Give the form of the adjective in parentheses that agrees with the noun in **bold type**. Remember that adjectives agree in case, number, and gender with the noun they modify. (Hint: the nouns decline like *hestr* 'horse' and the adjectives decline like *góðr* 'good', 1.2.)

a. Hann hafði ('had') góðan (góðr) **hest**.

b. Hon var dóttir **Álfs**, __________ (ágætr) **manns**.

c. Hann var __________ (ríkr) **konungr** ok __________ (vitr).

d. Gunnarr hljóp af ('leapt off') __________ (hvítr) **hesti**.

Lesson 2 Supplementary Exercises

1. Write the stressed vowels of the Old Icelandic words in the space provided.

frændi ___, Herjólfsson ___, kona ___, efniligsti ___, Reykjaness ___, Drepstokki ___, Bárðarson ___

2. Write the long vowels in the Old Icelandic words in the space provided.

Herjólfr ___, frændi ___, Ingólfr ___, landnámamaðr ___, hét ___

3. Fill in the appropriate endings.

a. Þorstein___ var mikil___ mað___. Hann var Egil___son, Skalla-Grím___son___.

b. Repeat exercise **a**, making Grímr the son of Egill and Egill the son of Þorsteinn.

____

____

4. Translate the sentences in exercise **3**.

a. ____

____

b. ____

____

5. Decline the strong masculine nouns *ormr* 'snake' and *vinr* 'friend' in the singular and the strong adjective *vænn* 'fine' in the masculine singular. (Hint: *vinr* takes the genitive in *-ar*.)

	Masc noun		Masc adj
***Sg** nom*	ormr	vinr	vænn
acc			
dat			
gen			

6. Give the case (nom., acc., or gen.) of the underlined noun or adjective.

a. Hrafnkell _nom._ bygði allan ________ dalinn.

b. Þeir þurfa góðs ________ hests ________.

c. Þórólfr ________ tók hring ________ Þorsteins ________.

7. Supply the nominative or genitive form of the missing masculine singular noun or adjective.

a. _Herjólfr_ (Herjólfr) hét maðr.

b. _______ (Egill) hafði land numit milli _______ (dalr) ok hofs.

c. Þeir koma ('come') til _______ (ríkr) _________ (maðr).

d. Álfr var __________ (mikill) __________ (hersir).

e. Þeir þurfa _______ (vitr) ____________ (konungr).

8. Decline the noun *maðr* 'man' in the singular and plural.

	Sing	Pl
nom	maðr	menn
acc		
dat		
gen		

9. Translate the following sentences.

a. Hrafnkell var vinr Freys.

____

b. Gunnlaugr var ójafnaðarmaðr.

____

c. Gunnlaugr tók hest Hrafnkels.

____

d. Hestr Hrafnkels var mikill ok góðr.

____

e. Freyr gaf Gunnlaugi orm.

____

10. Word search. Find the Old Icelandic words and translate them into English.

```
H A V I T R N A F N
E A L K O N U N G R
H I F L V I L D I H
L D G A R Y F I R O
U M H I O F A G R F
T I Ǫ E V D A L R K
R K T P R I F V X A
B I G A F S N A T L
A L M J Ǫ K I R Ǫ L
Æ L L A N D S R F A
```

allr ______________
dalr ______________
eigi ______________
fagr ______________
gaf ______________
hafa ______________
hersir ______________
hlutr ______________
hof ______________
kalla ______________
konungr ______________
land ______________
mikill ______________
mjǫk ______________
nafn ______________
var ______________
vildi ______________
vinr ______________
vitr ______________
yfir ______________

Lesson 3 Supplementary Exercises

1. Fill in the appropriate endings.

a. Konung___ hét Harald___. Hann var son___ Hálfdanar in___ góð___.
b. Dóttir Harald___ hét Ásgerð___, móðir Helg___ in___ sigrsæl___.
c. Elfráð___ var fyrst___ einvaldskonung___ í England___.
d. Harald___ var in___ fyrst___ konung___ yfir Nóreg___.
e. Egil___ var hǫfðing___; hann var hersi___ konungs.
f. Hákon var son___ Álf___ in___ mikl___.
g. Eirík___ var sonr Harald___ in___ góð___, hersi___ rík___ í Nóreg___.
h. Hann var fóstr___ Aðalstein___, rík___ goð___ ok væn___; Aðalstein___ var son___ Álf___ in___ mikl___.
i. Játvarð___ in___ væn___ var góð___ mað___ ok sigrsæl___.

2. Translate the sentences in exercise **1**.

a. ____
____
b. ____
____
c. ____
d. ____
e. ____
f. ____
g. ____
____
h. ____
____
i. ____
____

3. Supply suitable personal names, nouns, and adjectives.

a. _________i inn _________i hét _________r. Hann var _________r _________r ok _________n, _________r maðr ok _________r.

b. _________l inn _________i hét _________r. Hann var sonr _________a ins _________a, _________s _________s ok _________s.

4. Translate your answers to exercise **3**.

a. ____

____

____

b. ____

____

____

5. Decline the personal names *Ásvaldr, Eiríkr,* and *Þorsteinn*, and the place name *Nóregr*.

nom	Ásvaldr	Eiríkr	Þorsteinn	Nóregr
acc				
dat				
gen				

6. The following sentences are based on the reading selection, but the words are in jumbled order. Put the words into their proper order, declining the adjectives to agree with the nouns they modify.

Ex: fyrstr / hann / yfir / Englandi/ ganga / var / einvaldskonungr

Hann var fyrstr einvaldskonungr yfir Englandi.

a. Englandi / ríkr / fyrir/ reð / inn / Elfráðr

____

b. fóstra / hann / Hákonar /var / góðr / ins

____

c. bjó / sjónlítill/ ok/ í / maðr / Þórarinn / hét / er / Sunnudal

____

____

7. Decline the weak masculine nouns *bogi* ''bow' and *goði* 'chieftan' in the singular, and decline the definite article with the weak masculine forms of the adjective *hvítr* 'white'.

	Weak masc nouns		Article with weak masc adj	
Sg nom	bogi	goði	inn	hvíti
acc				
dat				
gen				

8. Translate the following sentences into Old Icelandic:

a. A man was named Egill; he lived at Borg in Borgarfjord.

b. Asvald took the *goðorð* over them.

c. Eirik was wealthy; he was the son of Norway's king. (Hint: *sonr* does not need the article when followed by a genitive.)

d. He gave Herjolf a ring.

9. Vocabulary training.

Across
1 after
3 father
5 victorious
6 days (dat. pl.)
7 foster-father
9 good
10 powerful, mighty

Down
2 ruled, governed
3 first
4 king
7 before
8 the

Lesson 4 Supplementary Exercises

1. Fill in the appropriate endings.

a. Ek vil gef__ þér skip___ (def.).

b. Þeir Bjǫrn ok Grím__ geng__ ofan til in__ góð__ skip__.

c. England er i__ fegrst__ land.

d. "Þá vil ek horf__ á skip___ (def.)," mælti fóstr__.

e. Á dǫgum Helg__ in__ ágæt__ mæl___ Þórólf__: "Vandliga hygg__ þú at skip____ (def.), konungsson."

f. Egil__ fór til Nóreg__, stór__ land__ ok fagr__.

g. Hann gekk til in__ litl__ hús__ ('house', neut.).

h. Þeir geng__ til Grím__, fóstr__ Harald__.

i. Eirík__ var in__ mest__ hofðing__. Skip hans var i__ mest__ skip.

2. Translate the sentences in exercise **1**.

a. ______________________________

b. ______________________________

c. ______________________________

d. ______________________________

e. ______________________________

____

f. ______________________________

g. ______________________________

h. ______________________________

i. ______________________________

____

3. Decline the two-syllable adjectives *auðigr* 'rich' and *mikill* 'big' in the masculine and neuter singular.

a. Strong.

	Masc		**Neut**	
Sg *nom*	auðigr	mikill	auðigt	mikit
acc				
dat				
gen				

b. Weak.

	Masc		Neut	
Sg *nom*	auðgi	mikli	auðga	mikla
acc				
dat				
gen				

4. Provide a definite article for each Old Icelandic word. Then match the phrase with its English translation by drawing a line between them.

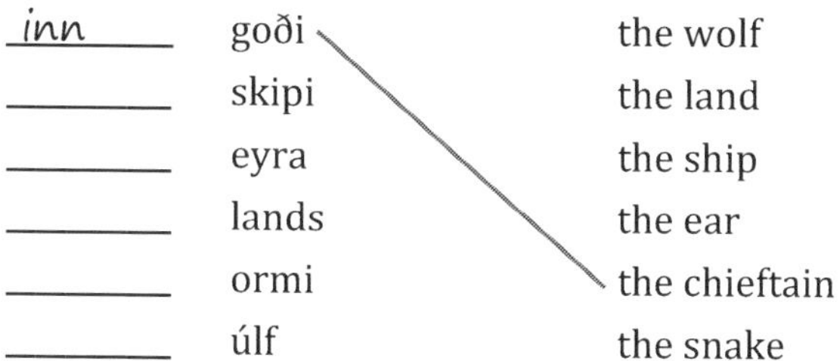

inn	goði	the wolf
______	skipi	the land
______	eyra	the ship
______	lands	the ear
______	ormi	the chieftain
______	úlf	the snake

5. Supply the appropriate form of the adjective. (Hint: recall from 3.2 that an adjective is weak when preceded by the article.)

a. inn góði (góðr) maðr

b. ________ (skarpr) sverðs

c. ins ________ (fagr) skips

d. inum ________ (ríkr) boga

e. ________ (langr) land

f. ins ________ (samr) árs

6. Decline the nouns *hestr* 'horse', *nafn* 'name', *fóstri* 'foster-father', and *eyra* 'ear' with suffixed article.

	Strong		Weak	
	Masc	**Neut**	**Masc**	**Neut**
Sg *nom*	hestrinn	nafnit	fóstrinn	eyrat
acc				
dat				
gen				

7. The following sentences are based on Reading Selection 4, but the words are in jumbled order. Put the words into their proper order, conjugating the verbs to agree with their subjects and supplying the appropriate case endings of the nouns.

Ex: skipsins / Bjǫrn / ofan / Þórólfr / ok / til / ganga

Þórólfr ok Bjǫrn gengu ofan til skipsins.

a. skipit / konungsson / Eiríkr / ganga / á / út

____

b. hyggja / vandliga / skipit / þú / at

____

c. þá / ek / skipit / gefa / vilja / þér

____

8. The following sentences are taken from Reading Selection 4. Fill in the blanks with the appropriate word from the box.

gekk ~~ofan~~ skipinu ~~skipsins~~ út vandliga vill þér

Ex: Þórólfr ok Bjǫrn gengu _ofan_ til _skipsins_.

a. Eiríkr konungsson __________ stundum á skipit __________.

b. __________ hyggr þú at __________, konungsson.

c. Þá __________ ek gefa __________ skipit.

9. Decline the following phrases in the indefinite and the definite.

a. Indefinite.

	a big king	a big ship
nom.	mikill konungr	mikit skip
acc.		
dat.		
gen.		

b. Definite.

	the big king	the big ship
nom.	inn mikli konungr	it mikla skip
acc.		
dat.		
gen.		

10. Translate the following sentences.

a. The ship was very big.

____

b. Helgi went onto a ship.

____

c. Helgi went onto the ship.

____

d. He went onto the big ship.

____

e. He stood on the big ship.

____

f. Thorolf said: "I want to travel to Norway."

____

g. Hrafnkel took Hakon's horse and gave the horse to Eirik.

____

Lesson 5 Supplementary Exercises

1. Fill in the appropriate forms of the masculine singular 3rd person pronoun *hann*.

a. ________ sér ('sees'), at konungr var þar. (NB: konungr without the art. often means 'the king'.)

b. Þeir gengu til Baldrs, ok sá ('saw') fegrð ________.

c. ________ stóð þar ok horfði á skipit.

d. Inn ungi maðr er vænn, ok allir lofa ________.

e. Þá var ________ konungr í Englandi.

f. Þórdís gekk nú til ________.

g. Þat var sagt ________, at konungr væri þar. (NB: væri 'was', subjunctive following the verb segja.)

h. Skipit vil ek gefa ________.

i. Þeir sá ('saw') ________ á skipinu.

2. Translate the sentences in exercise **1**.

a. ______________________________

b. ______________________________

c. ______________________________

d. ______________________________

e. ______________________________

f. ______________________________

g. ______________________________

h. ______________________________

i. ______________________________

3. State the case form of *hann* in each of the sentences in exercise **1**, and briefly state why each case is chosen.

a. ______________________________

b. ______________________________

c. ______________________________

d. ______________________________

e. ______________________________

f. ______________________________

g. ______________________________

h. ______________________________

i. ______________________________

4. Supply the Old Norse personal pronoun (*hann, hon, þat,* etc.) that matches the gender and case of the noun. (Hint: the Old Norse pronoun reflects the noun's gender no matter how it is translated in English.)

a. sverðit _þat_
b. boginn __________
c. kýrin __________
d. landsins __________
e. konungsins __________
f. úlfinum __________
g. skipinu __________

5. Give the past-tense stem of the following weak verbs. (Hint: some employ a vocalic link before the past-tense dental suffix [*-ð-* or a variant *-d-* or *-t-*] while others add the dental suffix directly to the root.)

svara	_svarað-_	horfa	__________
kalla	__________	kasta	__________
lifa	__________	fœða	__________
elska	__________	jafna	__________

6. Give the past-tense form of the weak verb in parentheses.

a. Hrafnkell _elskaði_ (elska) eigi annat goð meir en Frey.
b. Hon __________ (spyrja), "Hvar bygði ormrinn?"
c. Þær __________ (sleika) hrímsteina.
d. Loki __________ (kveðja) þann dverg ('that dwarf') er hét Andvari.
e. Nú __________ (mæla) Þorgerðr við manninn.
f. Þá __________ (senda) þeir Loka at sœkja gullit ('to seek the gold').

7. Translate the sentences in exercise **6**.

a. _Hrafnkel loved no other god more than Frey._

b. ______________________________

c. ______________________________

d. ______________________________

e. ______________________________

f. ______________________________

8. Rewrite the following 3 sing. present-tense verbs in the past tense. (Hint: all of these are weak verbs with vowel alternation.)

hann dvelr:	hann ________	hann spyrr:	hann ________
hann mylr:	hann ________	hann temr:	hann ________
hann segir:	hann ________	hann velr:	hann ________

9. Indicate whether the verb is singular or plural, then match the verb with its English translation by drawing a line between them.

pl.	horfðu	[they] bought
_____	vakti	[they] looked
_____	þakði	[it] crushed
_____	keyptu	[she] woke
_____	tamdi	[he] thatched
_____	muldi	[she] tamed
_____	fluttu	[they] conveyed

10. Word search. Find the Old Icelandic words and translate them into English.

```
F K O M A H M N K A
F Y R S T R S G B N
D R A U P V K L Z N
J O B E Æ K I E V A
N Z Y F L Œ P P M R
A I Y L O B T J U R
K F H A Ð K A A N G
V F V H N Æ S T A S
K N A S T E I N N X
M O T H H V A R V R
```

af ________	glepja ________	muna ________
annarr ________	hvar ________	næst ________
draup ________	hvat ________	skipta ________
efla ________	koma ________	steinn ________
fyrsta ________		

Lesson 6 Supplementary Exercises

1. The verbs in the following sentences are all in the past tense. Based on its form, state whether the underlined verb is weak or strong.

a. En þá er Hrafnkell hafði __weak__ land numit, þá efldi ________ hann blót mikil.

b. Hrafnkell bygði ________ allan dalinn ok gaf ________ mǫnnum land, ok tók ________ goðorð yfir þeim.

c. Þá mælti ________ Gangleri: "Hvar bygði ________ Ymir? eða við hvat lifði ________ hann?"

d. Þá er hrímit draup ________, þar varð ________ af kýr sú er Auðhumla hét ________, en fjórar mjólkár runnu ________ ór spenum hennar, ok fœddi ________ hon Ymi.

e. Eiríkr gekk ________ á land upp, stóð ________ þá ok horfði ________ á skipit.

2. Supply the appropriate forms of the verb *vera* in the pres. tense. (Hint: *synir* 'sons' is the plural of *sonr*.)

a. Ek _____ hersir mikill.
b. Hann _____ gǫfugr maðr.
c. Vér _____ Ósvaldssynir.
d. Þeir _____ Geitissynir.
e. Þér _____ Krakadœtr.
f. Þú _____ konungr ríkr.

3. Repeat exercise **2**, using past-tense forms of *vera*.

a. Ek _____ hersir mikill.
b. Hann _____ gǫfugr maðr.
c. Vér _____ Ósvaldssynir.
d. Þeir _____ Geitissynir.
e. Þér _____ Krakadœtr.
f. Þú _____ konungr ríkr.

4. The following strong verbs have different stems in the singular and plural of the past tense. For each verb, supply the missing past-tense form and the infinitive.

3 sing. past	3 pl. past	Infinitive
a. hann rann	þeir __runnu__	at __renna__
b. hon ________	þær gengu	at ________
c. hann skaut	þeir ________	at ________
d. þat ________	þau kómu	at ________
e. hon bar	þær ________	at ________
f. hann bjó	þeir ________	at ________

5. Provide suitable personal names, nouns, and adjectives.

___________i _____n _________i hét _________r. Hann var sonr ___________s _____s _________a, _________s ________s ok _________s.

6. Repeat exercise **5**, interchanging the two names and using different adjectives.

____

____

____

7. The following sentences are taken from R.S. 6.6. Fill in the blanks with the appropriate word from the box.

kom hét ins bjó maðr honum keypti hvíta ~~var~~

Ex: Hann _var_ sonr Þorgils Þorsteinssonar, Ǫlvis sonar, Ásvalds sonar, Øxna-Þóris sonar.

a. Þar hefjum vér þenna þátt, er sá ____________ bjó at Hofi í Vápnafirði er Helgi ____________.

b. Þorsteinn hvíti ____________ fyrst út til Íslands þeira langfeðga ok bjó at Toptavelli fyrir útan Síreksstaði.

c. En Steinbjǫrn ___________ at Hofi, sonr Refs ___________ rauða.

d. Ok er ____________ eyddisk fé fyrir þegnskapar sakar, þá ____________ Þorsteinn Hofs land ok bjó þar sex tigu vetra.

e. Hann átti Ingibjǫrgu Hróðgeirsdóttur ins ____________.

8. Translate the sentences in exercise **7**.

a. ____

____

b. ____

____

____

c. ____

d. ____

____

____

e. ____

____

9. Give the translation of the following adjectives.

dauðr ____________

frægr ____________

fríðr ____________

fullr ____________

heill ____________

illr ____________

kyrr ____________

lítill ____________

reiðr ____________

sterkr ____________

stórr ____________

ungr ____________

vándr ____________

vinsæll ____________

10. Complete the following declesions.

a. nom. vinsæll maðr
acc. ______________________
dat. ______________________
gen. ______________________

b. nom. inn vinsæli maðr
acc. ______________________
dat. ______________________
gen. ______________________

c. nom. ______________________
acc. ______________________
dat. ______________________
gen. góðs vinar

d. nom. ______________________
acc. ______________________
dat. ______________________
gen. ins góða vinar

e. nom. ______________________
acc. illan óvin
dat. ______________________
gen. ______________________

f. nom. ______________________
acc. inn illa óvin
dat. ______________________
gen. ______________________

g. nom. ______________________
acc. ______________________
dat. ungu barni
gen. ______________________

h. nom. ______________________
acc. ______________________
dat. inu unga barni
gen. ______________________

Lesson 7 Supplementary Exercises

1. Fill in the appropriate endings.

a. Þú mátt mark__ fegrð inna mikl__ ás__.

b. Baldr heit___ in__ fegrst__ ás__.

c. Baldr in__ hvít__ er son__ Óðin__ in__ vitr__.

d. Land___ (def.) er all___ land__ fegrst.

e. Ásgerð__ sagð__, at hár hans er fagr__.

f. Frá skip____ (def.) er gott at segj____.

g. Hann bý__ þar, sem heit___ Breiðablik. Þat e__ á himn__.

h. Gísl__ var in__ fegrst__ hersi__ á Nóreg__.

2. Translate the following sentences.

a. Thorolf owned a white ship.

____

b. Thorolf's ship was of all ships (the) best.

____

c. Ingibjorg saw a little child.

____

d. The sun rises and shines in heaven. (NB: *sólin* 'the sun')

____

3. Rewrite the following sentences in the pres. tense.

a. Þeir Þórólfr ok Bjǫrn stóðu þar.

____

b. Hann bjó á himni ok var vitrastr ásanna.

____

c. Þorsteinn var auðigr at fé.

____

4. Change the subject of the following sentences from *Þórólfr* to *Þeir Þórólfr* and make other necessary changes.

a. Þórólfr sitr með konungi.

____

b. Þórólfr býr í Haukadal.

____

c. Þórólfr stóð upp af bekkinum.

____

d. Þórólfr fór með skipinu.

____

e. Þórólfr náði konungs fundi.

____

5. Supply suitable personal names, nouns, and adjectives

a. ___________n hét __________l maðr. Hann var __________r at fé ok __________r.

b. __________l var ____________sson, ____________ssonar, __________s __________s ok __________s.

c. ___________l var __________n __________r ok __________r.

6. Translate your answers to exercise **5**.

a. ____

____

b. ____

____

c. ________________________________

7. At this point in the readings, you have encountered several weak verbs which employ a vocalic link before the past-tense dental suffix. Give the 3rd person singular past of the following verbs.

lofa	lofaði	skapa	______
marka	______	tala	______
kasta	______	jafna	______
smíða	______	svara	______

8. Translate the noun or adjective and supply the requested genitive forms.

Ex.: sverð sword

gen. sg. sverðs gen. pl. sverða

a. allr ______

masc. gen. sg. (strong): ______ masc. gen. sg. (weak) ______

gen. pl. (strong) ______

b. góðr ______

neut. gen. sg. (strong): ______ neut. gen. sg. (weak) ______

gen. pl. (strong) ______

c. konungr ______

gen. sg. ______ gen. pl. ______

9. Supply the superlative form of the adjective given in parentheses.

a. Þat er allra grasa ______ (hvítr).

b. It ______ (hvítr) gras er jafnat til Baldrs brár.

c. Baldr er ______ (vitr) ok ______ (líknsamr) ásanna.

d. Skip Þórólfs var allra skipa ______ (fagr).

e. "It ______ (fagr) er skipit," segir Eiríkr.

f. Hringr Sigurðs var inn ______ (góðr).

10. Supply the suffixed definite article.

	Strong		**Weak**	
	Masc	**Neut**	**Masc**	**Neut**
Sg *nom*	áss inn	gras it	goði nn	auga t
acc	ás___	gras___	goða___	auga___
dat	ási___	grasi___	goða___	auga___
gen	áss___	grass___	goða___	auga___
Pl *gen*	ása___	grasa___	goða___	augna___

11. Word search. Find the Old Icelandic words and translate them into English.

P G U X B H V T V Z E T A L A
A Y P K E T G L M T S Ý G M U
H I M I N N Y V H E D G R Z S
E U L F O R R Z E F G D A R E
F V J F Z N F V Z R J A S E G
J J E K B Æ Ð I E T I T U A J
Z U Ð R Ý T J R F T U T J Y A
T E F N A D T A S O L I Ð M V
G I S L E X Þ V F E K O J A I
U T Æ X Y F I O R N M Œ F O T
U T T K M A P Y V F A I Ð A R
L B E Z T R Á H L Ý S I R T A
G J Z Þ Y V U K H E I T I R S
U O A U G H U F X S E S M H T
Z D H H E I T A Æ Z F A J J R

beztr ____________
bæði ____________
eitt ____________
gras ____________
heita ____________
heitir ____________
himinn ____________
jafna ____________
lofa ____________
lýsir ____________
mega ____________
segja ____________
sem ____________
tala ____________
vera ____________
verit ____________
vitrastr ____________

Lesson 8 Supplementary Exercises

1. Fill in the appropriate endings.

a. Egil__ stóð upp af in__ stór__ bekk ok kvadd__ mann____ (def.).
b. Gísl__ bjó í in__ fegrst__ firð__ á Ísland__.
c. Svíarnir fór__ til in__ gaml__ skip__.
d. Bjǫrn stóð upp ok gekk af fund_____ (def.).

2. Change the direct speech in the following sentences to indirect speech.

a. Þeir spyrja, "Hverr var maðrinn?"

____

b. Þeir segja, "Maðrinn var góðr."

____

3. Rewrite the sentences given in exercise **2**, changing *þeir* to *hann* and making other necessary changes.

a. ______________________________

b. ______________________________

4. Now rewrite the sentences in exercise **3** in the past tense.

a. ______________________________

b. ______________________________

5. Give the complete declension of the definite article (masculine, feminine, and neuter, in both singular and plural).

	Masc	**Fem**	**Neut**
Sg *nom*	______	______	______
acc	______	______	______
dat	______	______	______
gen	______	______	______
Pl *nom*	______	______	______
acc	______	______	______
dat	______	______	______
gen	______	______	______

6. Give the present participle and the past participle stem of the following weak verbs.

	Pres. Part.	Past Part. Stem
a. segja	segjandi	sagð-
b. gera	______	______
c. tala	______	______
d. kalla	______	______

7. Write the 3 sing. pres. perfect and the 3 sing. past perfect tenses of the verbs in exercise **6**, then translate the phrases.

	Pres. Perfect	Past Perfect
a. segja	hann hefir sagt	hann hafði sagt
	he has said	he had said

b. gera þat ________________ þat ________________

________________ ________________

c. tala hun ________________ hun ________________

________________ ________________

d. kalla hann ________________ hann ________________

________________ ________________

8. The following sentences are based on the reading selections, but the words are in jumbled order. Put the words into their proper order, conjugating the verbs to agree with their subjects and supplying the appropriate case endings of the nouns.

Ex: fyrir / konungr / Óláfr / ráða / Svíþjóð / sœnskr / tími / þessi

Þenna tíma réð fyrir Svíþjóð Óláfr konungr sœnski.

a. Gunnlaugr / koma / nær / til / um / Uppsalir / várit / þing

____

b. hann / hverr / Óláfr / spyrja / vera

____

c. af / bekkr / fyrir / ganga / inn / konungr / maðr / ok / óœðri / standa / upp

____

____

d. á / beztr / hann / Ísland / inn / vera / ætt

____

e. Aðalsteinn / Egill / inn / með / mestr / ok / skiljask / vinátta

____

9. Complete the Old Icelandic sentences by supplying a translation of the words and phrases underlined in English.

a. We <u>traveled</u> to <u>England</u> with <u>Eirik and his companions</u>.

Vér __________ til ____________ við ____________.

b. You <u>built</u> the <u>greatest temple</u>.

Þú __________ it ____________.

c. Helgi <u>and his companions</u> <u>stood up</u> from the <u>lower bench</u>.

________ Helgi ______________ af inum ______________.

10. Supply the past-tense form of the verbs and the appropriate form of the adjectives in parentheses. (Hint: remember that adjectives preceded by a definite article take the weak form.)

a. Ek _______ (taka) boga __________ (mikill).

b. Hon _______ (eiga) _______ (lítill) hús.

c. Vér __________ (mæla) við inn _________ (auðigr) goða.

d. Hon __________ (kveðja) ___________ (sterkr) konung.

e. Þú ________ (koma) við it __________ (skarpr) sverð.

f. Þér ________ (taka) inn _________ (rauðr) hring.

11. Vocabulary training.

Across
- 3 bench
- 4 greeted (3sg past)
- 7 took (3sg past)
- 8 Icelandic
- 9 light, fair
- 10 himself

Down
- 1 great
- 2 assembly
- 3 book
- 5 bravest
- 6 family

Lesson 9 Supplementary Exercises

1. Fill in the appropriate endings.

a. Yngvar__ gekk nú til skút__ góð____ ok hvít___.

b. Skút__ hans var all___ skút__ fegrst.

c. Rewrite exercise **1.a**, replacing 'boat' with 'ship'.

____

d. Rewrite exercise **1.b**, replacing 'boat' with 'ship'.

____

e. Hǫfðing____ (def.) bað Helg__ in____ ágæt____, dótt___ Gísl__.

f. Elfráð__ bað Þór__, syst___ Harald__.

g. Þorkel__ Súrsson_ bið__ þess_____ kon__ ok get__ han__ at eiga.

h. Helg__ in__ stór__ átti Æs__ in__ væn__, rík__ kon__ ok gǫfg__.

i. Helg__ in fagr__ hét kon__. Hon var dóttir Ásgerð___ in____ góð__, væn____ kon__ ok ágæt____.

j. Þeir Þorstein__ ok Egil__ fór__ til Ísland__ þat sam__ haust.

2. Translate the sentences in exercise **1**.

a. ____________________

b. ____________________

c. ____________________

d. ____________________

e. ____________________

____

f. ____________________

g. ____________________

____

h. ____________________

____

i. ____________________

____

j. ____________________

3. Supply suitable personal names and adjectives. (NB: Do not use *fagr*.)

a. ________i inn ________i hét faðir ________u innar ________u ok ________a ins ________a.

b. ________a in ________a hét dóttir ________a ins ________a ok ________u innar ________u.

c. ________i inn ________i hét faðir ________u innar ________u ok ________a ins ________a.

4. Repeat exercise **3**, substituting names of strong noun form for all names of weak noun form.

a. ____________________

____

b. ____________________

____

c. ____________________

____

5. Supply the appropriate form of the verb shown in parentheses.

Pres.	Past
ek _segi_ (segja)	ek _sagði_ (segja)
þú ________ (hafa)	þú ________ (hafa)
hann ______ (vera)	hann ______ (vera)
vér ________ (senda)	vér ________ (senda)
þér ________ (lifa)	þér ________ (lifa)

þær __________ (skjóta) þær _________ (skjóta)

6. The following sentences are from R.S. 9, but the words are in jumbled order. Put the words into their proper order, conjugating verbs to agree with their subjects and supplying the appropriate case forms of nouns. Hint: you may wish to refer back to the reading selection.

a. ríkr / Bjǫrn / Sogn / hersir / í / er / á / búa / Aurland / heita

____

b. at / Bjǫrn/ Firðir / fjǫlmennr / í / nǫkkurr / staddr / vera / veizla

____

____

c. hefja / Þóra / Bjǫrn / sinn / upp / bónorð / biðja / ok

____

d. nema / Bjǫrn / sér / á / heim / ok / á brott / Þóra / hafa / með / Aurland.

____

____

7. Translate the sentences in exercise **6**.

a. ____

____

b. ____

____

c. ____

____

d. ____

____

8. Conjugate the weak verb *gera* 'make, do' and the strong verb *bera* 'carry, bear' in the present and past tenses.

	Pres		**Past**	
	Weak	**Strong**	**Weak**	**Strong**
	gera	**bera**	**gera**	**bera**
1sg	________	________	________	________
2sg	________	________	________	________
3sg	________	________	________	________
1pl	________	________	________	________
2pl	________	________	________	________
3pl	________	________	________	________

9. Decline the following phrases in the indefinite and definite.

a. Indefinite

	a young horse	an Icelandic saga	a white ship
nom.	ungr hestr	íslenzk saga	hvítt skip
acc.	______	______	______
dat.	______	______	______
gen.	______	______	______

b. Definite

	the young horse	the Icelandic saga	the white ship
nom.	______	______	______
acc.	______	______	______
dat.	______	______	______
gen.	______	______	______

10. Complete the Old Icelandic sentences by supplying a translation of the words and phrases underlined in English.

a. Ingibjorg was <u>a Swedish woman</u>.

Ingibjǫrg var ______________.

b. She was <u>wise</u> in her <u>old age</u>.

Hon var ________ í _______ sinni.

c. Her <u>brother</u> <u>was married to Thora the Red</u>.

__________ hennar ______________________________.

d. <u>Thora</u> came from <u>a most noble family</u>.

_________ kom frá ______________________.

e. <u>They (fem.) lived</u> in <u>Norway</u>.

__________________ í __________.

Saga of Ragnar Lodbrok
Introduction

The following four readings are drawn from the *Saga of Ragnar Lodbrok* (*Ragnars saga loðbrókar*). *Ragnar's Saga* is a legendary saga, a category of Icelandic prose stories known today as *fornaldar-sögur* ('sagas of ancient times'). In most instances, the *fornaldar sögur* tell of people and events in Scandinavia before Iceland's settlement in the ninth century. Such tales were written down in Iceland mainly in the thirteenth and fourteenth centuries, long after the Viking Age events which they describe. The *fornaldar sögur* vary considerably among themselves, but most originate in ancient oral tellings. As a saga genre, they mix legend, history, folklore, myth, and storyteller invention.

Ragnar's saga tells that Ragnar Lodbrok (*Loðbrók* means 'Hairy-Breeches') was a Viking chief in the early ninth century. As with many *fornaldar-sögur, Ragnar's Saga* is a late and not very trustworthy source. With this in mind, it is one of our few sources recounting events from Ragnar's life, including a series of Viking attacks on England that he led.

According to the saga, Ragnar is captured in England by King Ælla of Northumbria (*Ella* in Old Norse) and dies a gruesome death in Ella's snake pit. Ragnar's sons, Bjorn Ironsides (*Bjǫrn járnsíða*), Ivar the Boneless (*Ívarr beinlausi*), Sigurd Snake-in-the-Eye (*Sigurðr ormr í auga*),[1] Ubbi and Hvitserk (*Hvítserkr* 'White Shirt') receive the news of their father's death and quickly vow vengeance.

The sons assemble a large fleet and set out with their Viking army to conquer England, which at the time was divided into several independent and often hostile Old English kingdoms. As described by Anglo-Saxon chroniclers, the "Great Heathen Army" lands in East Anglia and soon makes its way north. In 866, the sons, led by Ivarr the Boneless, conquer York (*Jorvík*). The next year the sons defeat King Ælla.

This time, it is Ælla's turn to die a gruesome death. According to the saga, the sons take their vengeance on the Northumbrian king by performing on him the blood-eagle (*blóðǫrn*). The sons cut open King Ælla's back and pull out his lungs. In this way, the king dies resembling an eagle in flight as his lungs fill with air and his ribs move. The Anglo-Saxon Chronicle does not mention the blood eagle, but it does recount that King Ælla died in battle in 867 while leading his army at York.

---

[1] **Sigurðr ormr í auga**: 'Sigurd Snake-in-the-Eyes', one of Ragnar's children who was prophesied by his mother to have image of a snake biting its own tail in his eyes.

Ór *Ragnars sǫgu loðbrókar* (15. kap.)

(From the *Saga of Ragnar Lodbrok*, Chap. 15)

1. Ragnar Lodbrok Sails His Ships to England

Nú heldr Ragnarr skipum sínum[2] til Englands, sem hann hafði ætlat. Honum gaf byri hvassa,[3] svá at við England brýtr hann báða knǫrru sína,[4] en á land komsk allt lið hans, ok heldu klæðum sínum ok vápnum.[5] Ok þar, sem hann kemr við þorp ok borgir ok kastala,[6] þá vinnr hann.

En konungr sá hét Ella, er þá réð Englandi. Hann hafði haft fréttir til Ragnars,[7] er hann fór ór landi. Hann hafði sett menn fyrir,[8] at hann skyldi þegar vita, er herrinn kœmi[9] við land. Nú fóru þeir menn til fundar við Ellu konung ok segja honum hersǫgu. Nú lætr hann senda boð um allt sitt ríki ok bað til sín koma hvern mann, er skildi má valda ok hesti ríða[10] ok þori at berjask, ok dregr hann saman svá mikinn her, at furða var at.[11] Nú búask þeir til bardaga Ella konungr.[12]

Þá mælti Ella konungr við lið sitt: "Ef vér sigrumsk í bardaga þessum ok verði þér við þat varir,[13] at Ragnarr er kominn, þá skulu þér eigi bera vápn á hann, því at hann á þá sonu eptir, er aldri munu af oss ganga, ef hann fellr."

Translate: ____

____

____

____

____

---

[2] **skipum sínum:** 'his ships' (dat. pl., see 12.3.4).

[3] **Honum gaf byri hvassa**: 'He got (*lit.* to him [it] gave, *impers.*) fierce winds' (acc. pl., see 12.3.1; 13.1).

[4] **báða knǫrru sína:** 'both his ships'(acc. pl., see 14.3; 17.6).

[5] **klæðum sínum ok vápnum:** 'their clothes and weapons' (dat. pl., see 12.3.3; 14.3).

[6] **þorp ok borgir ok kastala:** 'villages and towns and castles' (all acc. pl., see 12.3; 12.4).

[7] **Hann hafði haft fréttir til Ragnars**: 'He had had news (acc. pl., see 12.3.2) of Ragnar'.

[8] **Hann hafði sett menn fyrir:** 'He had set men to watch'.

[9] **kœmi:** 'came', 3sg. past subjunct. of *koma* 'come' (see 16.1).

[10] **skildi ... valda ok hesti ríða** 'wield a shield and ride a horse': both *valda* 'wield' and *ríða* 'ride' take a dat. obj.

[11] **furða var at:** 'it was a wonder'.

[12] **þeir ... Ella konungr:** 'King Ella and his men'.

[13] **verði þér við þat varir:** 'you become aware' (*lit.* '[it] becomes aware to you of it', *impers.*); *verði*, 3sg pres, subjunct. of *verða* 'become' (see 15.5).

Vocabulary

aldri *adv* never
á (*inf* **eiga**) *vb* has
bardagi *m* battle
báðir (*acc m* báða) *adj/pron pl* both
boð *n* bidding, command; message
borg (*pl* -ir) *f* stronghold, town
brjóta (brýtr; braut, brutu; brotinn) *vb* break; wreck (*a ship*)
brýtr (*inf* **brjóta**) *vb* breaks
búa (býr; bjó, bjoggu; búinn) *vb* live (in a place), dwell; *refl* **búask** prepare (oneself); **búask til** prepare (oneself) for
byrr (*pl acc* byri) *m* fair wind; **honum gaf byri hvassa** *impers* he got fierce winds
draga (dregr; dró, drógu; dreginn) *vb* pull, draw
dregr (*inf* **draga**) *vb* draws
eiga (á, eigu; átti; áttr) *vb* own, have (relatives); **eiga eptir** leave behind
Ella *m* Ælla, King of Northumbria (*personal name*)
falla (fellr; fell, fellu; fallinn) *vb* fall
fara (ferr; fór, fóru; farinn) *vb* go, travel
fellr (*inf* **falla**) *vb* falls
fór (*inf* **fara**) *vb* (he) went
fóru (*inf* **fara**) *vb* (they) went
frétt (*pl acc fréttir*) *f* news
fundr (*gen* -ar) *m* meeting; audience
furða *f* wonder, marvel
ganga (gengr; gekk, gengu; genginn) *vb* go; **ganga af** leave off, be finished with
halda (heldr; helt, heldu; haldinn) *vb* [*w acc/dat*] hold; hold on to, keep; direct, hold on a course
heldr (*inf* **halda**) *vb* holds
heldu (*inf* **halda**) *vb* (they) held, kept
herr *m* army, host
hersaga *f* war-tidings, news of war
hersǫgu *acc sg of* **hersaga**
hvass (*pl acc m* hvassa) *adj* sharp, keen; **honum gaf byri hvassa** *impers* he got fierce winds
hverr (*sg acc m* hvern) *indef pron* each, every

kastali *m* castle
kemr (*inf* **koma**) *vb* comes
klæði *n* garment, clothing
knǫrr (*pl acc* knǫrru) *m* ship
koma (kemr; kom, kómu; kominn) *vb* come; *refl* **komask** reach, arrive
komsk (*inf* **komask**, *see* **koma**) *vb* reached, arrived
kœmi (*inf* **koma**) *vb* came
láta (lætr; lét, létu; látinn) *vb* let, allow; [*w inf*] have (something) done
lætr (*inf* **láta**) *vb* has something done
má (*inf* **mega**) *vb* is able
mega (má, megu; mátti; mátt) *vb* be able
mikill (*acc m* mikinn) *adj* big, large, great
oss *acc/dat of* **vér**
ríða (ríðr; reið, riðu; riðinn) *vb* [*w dat*] ride
ríki *n* realm, kingdom
setja (-tt-) *vb* set, put, place; **setja [e-n] fyrir** order [sb] to keep watch
sigra (-að-) *vb* conquer, be victorious; *refl* **sigrask** gain victory
sigrumsk (*inf* **sigrask**, *see* **sigra**) *vb* (we) gain victory
sik *refl pron* himself
sín *refl pron* himself (*gen of* **sik**)
skildi *dat sg of* **skjǫldr**
skjǫldr (*dat* skildi) *m* shield
skulu (skal, skulu; skyldi) *vb* shall (necessity)
skyldi (*inf* **skulu**) *vb* should
sonr (*pl acc* sonu) *m* son
sonu *acc pl of* **sonr**
valda *vb* [*w dat*] wield, control
varr (*m pl* varir) *adj* aware; **verðr [e-m] varr við [e-t]** [sb] becomes aware of [sth]
vápn *n* weapon; **bera vápn á [e-n]** raise a weapon against [sb]
vera (er; var, váru; verit) *vb* be; **furða var at** it was a wonder
vér (*acc/dat* oss) *pron* we
við *prep* [*w acc*] with, to
vinna (vinnr; vann, unnu; unninn) *vb* win, overcome, conquer
vita (veit, vitu; vissi; vitaðr) *vb* know
þar *adv* there; **þar sem** there where
þá *acc of* **þeir**
þegar *adv* at once, immediately
þeir (*acc* þá) *dem pron/adj* those (*m*)
þessi (*sg dat m* þessum) *dem pron/adj* this (one)
þér *pron* you (*pl*)
þora (-ð-) *vb* dare, have courage
þorp *n* village, hamlet
því at *conj* because
ætla (-að-) *vb* intend

Lesson 10 Supplementary Exercises

1. Fill in the appropriate endings.

a. In__ veik__ bogi var brost____.

b. Rewrite sentence **a**, replacing *bogi* with *sverð* and making other necessary changes.

____

c. Rewrite sentence **a**, replacing *bogi* with *ǫr* and making other necessary changes.

____

2. Translate the sentences in exercise **1**.

a. ____________________________________

b. ____________________________________

c. ____________________________________

3. Decline the nouns *leggr* 'leg', *ey* 'ísland', and *ǫr* 'arrow' in the singular. (Hint: these nouns have stem-final *-j-* or *-v-*.)

	Masc	**Fem**	
	leggr (-j-)	**ey (-j-)**	**ǫr (-v-)**
Sg *nom*	leggr	ey	ǫr
acc			
dat			
gen			

4. Decline the adjectives *þriði* 'third' (weak only) and *døkkr* 'dark' (strong and weak) in the masc. singular. (Hint: these adjectives have stem-final *-j-* or *-v-*.)

	þriði (-j-)	**døkkr (-v-)**	
	Weak	**Strong**	**Weak**
Sg *nom*	þriði	døkkr	døkkvi
acc			
dat			
gen			

5. Rewrite the following sentences in the past tense.

a. Hann biðr. ________

b. Hann býr. ________

6. Rewrite the present-tense sentences in exercise **5** in reflexive form.

a. ________

b. ________

7. Rewrite your answers to exercise **5** (past tense) in reflexive form.

a. ________

b. ________

8. Translate the following sentences.

a. Þeir spyrja, hverr hann væri.

____

b. Þeir mæla við konung.

____

c. Þeir kasta sverðinu til konungs.

____

d. Segja þeir, at þessi maðr væri Finnskr?

____

9. Rewrite the Icelandic sentences in exercise **8**, replacing *þeir* with *hann* (see 7.6) and making other necessary changes.

Ex.: **a.** Hann spyrr, hverr hann væri.

b. ______

c. ______

d. ______

10. Rewrite the sentences in exercise **9** in the past tense.

Ex.: **a.** Hann spurði, hverr hann væri.

b. ______

c. ______

d. ______

11. Give the full declension of *fundinn* 'found' past participle of *finna*.

	Masc	Fem	Neut
Sg *nom*	fund______	fund______	fund______
acc	fund______	fund______	fund______
dat	fund______	fund______	fund______
gen	fund______	fund______	fund______
Pl *nom*	fund______	fund______	fund______
acc	fund______	fund______	fund______
dat	fund______	fund______	fund______
gen	fund______	fund______	fund______

The North Atlantic World of the Medieval Icelanders.

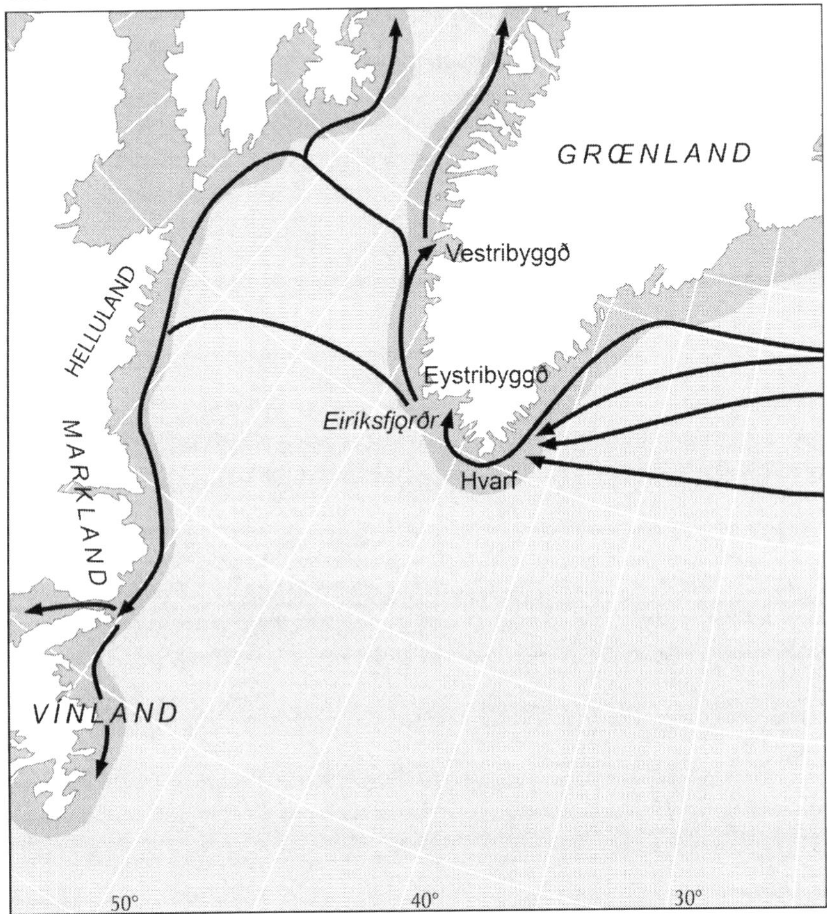

Svá segj___ vitrir menn, at ór Nóreg___ frá Stað___ sé sjau dœgr___ sigling í vestr til Horn___ á Ísland___ austanverð___, en frá Snæfellsnes___, þar er skemmst er, er fjǫgurra dœgr___ haf í vestr til Grœnland___. En svá er sag___, ef siglt er ór Bjǫrgyn rétt í vestr til Hvarf______ [def.] á Grœnland___, at þá mun siglt vera tylft fyrir sunnan Ísland. Frá Reykjanes___ á sunnanverð___ Ísland___ er fimm dœgr___ haf til Jǫlduhlaup___ á Írland___ (í suðr; en frá Langanes___ á norðanverð___ Ísland___ er) fjǫgurra dœgr___ haf norðr til Svalbarð___ í hafsbotn. (*Landnámabók*)

10°
0°
10°
Svalbarði
(= Jan Mayen ?)
70°
Snæfellsnes
Langanes
Þrándheimr
65°
ÍSLAND
Staðr
NÓREGR
SVÍÞJÓÐ
Bjǫrgyn
Horn
Reykjanes
Færeyjar
Hjaltland
Orkneyjar
DANMǪRK
60°
Suðreyjar
SKOTLAND
FRÍSLAND
ENGLAND
55°
Jǫlduhlaup
(Slyne Head)
ÍRLAND
NORÐMANDÍ
20°
10°

Translate: ____

____

____

____

____

____

____

____

____

____

____

____

____________________. (____________________)

Lesson 11 Supplementary Exercises

1. Umlaut.

a. Fill in the short vowels of Old Icelandic in the vowel space chart.

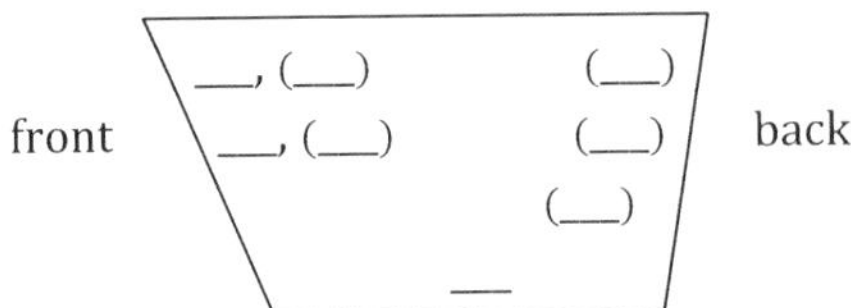

b. Fill in the long vowels of Old Icelandic in the vowel space chart.

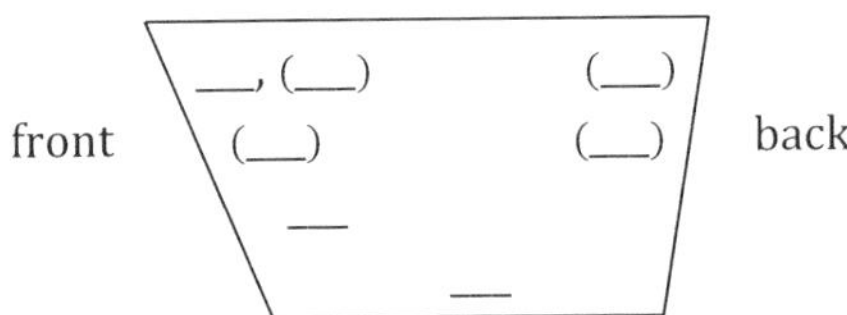

c. Fill in the missing vowels in the vowel space charts and draw arrows to show the effect of *i*-umlaut.

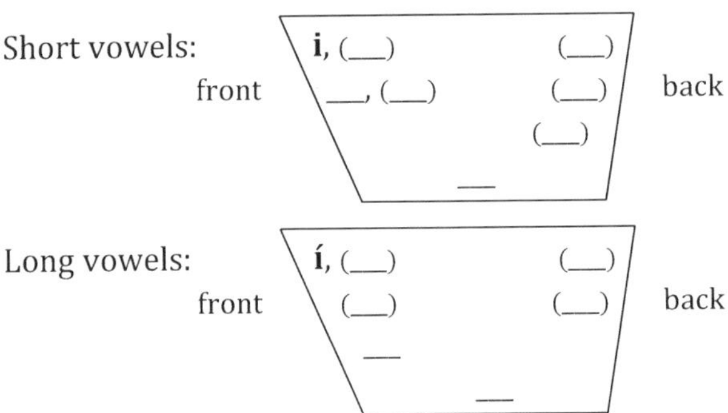

d. Fill in the missing vowels in the vowel space chart and draw an arrow to show the effect of *u*-umlaut.

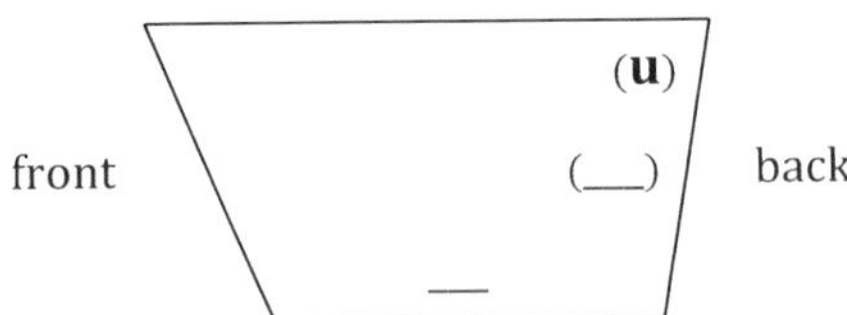

2. Fill in the appropriate endings.

a. Þeir deyj__ í búð_____ (def.).

b. Þeir skjót__ at inum mikl__ mann__ í krapparúm____ (def.).

c. Lǫng spjót fljúg__ ór skip____ (def.).

d. Þeir ráð__ fyrir i___ stór__ land__.

3. Rewrite the sentences in exercise **2**, changing the subject of each sentence from pl. to sing. and making other necessary changes.

a. ____

b. ____

____

c. ____

d. ____

4. Fill in the appropriate endings.

a. Hann bý___ nú á Arnarstakksheið___.

b. Barn kem___ til Jórsalaland___.

c. Hann gef___ honum i___ fegrst___ skip.

d. Hann høgg___ til in___ døkkv___ jǫtun___.

5. Rewrite the sentences in exercise **4**, changing the subject of each sentence to plural and making other necessary changes.

a. ____

b. ____

c. ____

d. ____

6. Write the 3 sing. and 3 pl. pres. forms of the following strong verbs.

at biðja:	hann ___________,	þeir ___________
at deyja:	hon ___________,	þær ___________
at drjúpa:	þat ___________,	þau ___________
at hǫggva:	hann ___________,	þeir ___________
at láta:	hann ___________,	þeir ___________
at syngja:	hon ___________,	þær ___________

7. Supply the 3 pl. pres. form that corresponds to the 3 sing. pres. form given. (Hint: these are all strong verbs with vowel alternation.)

hann blæss:	þeir ___________	þat heldr:	þau ___________
hon dregr:	þær ___________	hann hleypr:	þeir ___________
hon ekr:	þær ___________	hann ræðr:	þeir ___________
hann eykr:	þeir ___________	hon sefr:	þær ___________
hon grætr:	þær ___________	þat stendr:	þau ___________

8. Decline the fem. nouns *hǫnd* 'hand, *jǫrð* 'earth', and *saga* 'story' in the singular. (Hint: *hǫnd* shows *a*~*ǫ*~*e* alternation, while *jǫrð* and *saga* show *a*~*ǫ* alternation.)

Sg *nom*	hǫnd	jǫrð	saga
acc			
dat			
gen			

9. Decline the masculine nouns *kǫttr* 'cat', *lǫgr* 'sea', and *hjǫrtr* 'deer' in the singular. (Hint: *kǫttr* and *lǫgr* decline like *vǫllr*, and *hjǫrtr* declines like *skjǫldr*.)

Sg *nom*	kǫttr	lǫgr	hjǫrtr
acc	______	______	______
dat	______	______	______
gen	______	______	______

10. Decline the following saga titles and translate each phrase:

a. (nom.) Fóstbrœðra saga

____

(acc.) um ______________________________

____

(dat.) ór ______________________________

____

(gen.) til ______________________________

____

b. (nom.) Hrafnkels saga Freysgoða

____

(acc.) um ______________________________

____

(dat.) ór ______________________________

____

(gen.) til ______________________________

____

c. (nom.) Egils saga Skalla-Grímssonar

____

(acc.) um ______________________________

____

(dat.) ór ______________________________

____

(gen.) til ______________________________

____

d. (nom.) Gunnlaugs saga Ormstungu

____

(acc.) um ______________________________

____

(dat.) ór ______________________________

____

(gen.) til ______________________________

____

11. Fill in the appropriate endings and missing vowels in the following passage from *Ragnars saga loðbrókar*.

Nú f__r__ (past) þeir menn til fund___ við Ellu konung ok segj__ hon____ hers__g__. Nú l__t__ (pres.) hann send__ boð um all__ si___ rík__ ok bað til s__n koma hver__ mann, er sk__ld__ má vald__ ok hest__ ríð__ ok þori at berjask, ok dr__g__ (pres.) hann saman svá miki___ her, at furða var at. Nú bú__sk þeir til bardag__ Ella konungr.

12. Vocabulary training.

Across

2 power
3 (he) drew
6 shield
8 sword
9 (it) broke
10 (he) shot

Down

1 middle
3 dark
4 fight
5 loudly
7 arrow
10 a time

1
2
3
4
5
6
7
8
9
10

Ór *Ragnars sǫgu loðbrókar* (15. kap.)
(From the *Saga of Ragnar Lodbrok*, Chap. 15)

2. Ragnar Engages in Battle

Ragnarr býsk nú til bardaga, ok hann hafði þat klæði, er Randalín[14] hafði gefit honum at skilnaði, fyrir brynju ok þat spjót í hendi, er hann vann at orminum, er lá um sal Þóru, ok engi þorði annarra,[15] ok hann hafði enga hlíf nema hjálm. En þá er þeir hittask, tóksk bardagi.[16]

Ragnarr hafði miklu minna lið. Bardaginn hafði eigi lengi verit, áðr lið Ragnars fell mjǫk. En þar, sem hann fór, varð rýrt fyrir, ok gekk hann í gegnum fylkingar[17] þann dag, ok þar, sem hann hjó eða lagði í skjǫldu, brynjur eða hjálma,[18] þá váru svá stór hǫgg hans,[19] at ekki vætta[20] stóð við, en aldri var svá til hans hǫggvit eða skotit,[21] at neitt vápn yrði honum at meini,[22] ok fekk hann aldri sár, en hann drap mikinn fjǫlda af liði Ellu konungs.

Translate: ____

____

____

____

____

____

____

____

____

____

____

____

____

---

14 Ragnar's wife.

15 **engi ... annarra:** 'no one else' (*lit.* 'no one of others' [gen. pl., see 13.3]).

16 **En þá er þeir hittask, tóksk bardagi:** 'And then when they met, [the] battle began'.

17 **í gegnum fylkingar:** 'through [the] ranks' (acc. pl., see 12.3.2).

18 **í skjǫldu, brynjur eða hjálma:** 'into shields, mail coats or helmets' (all acc. pl., see 12.3.1; 12.4; 17.6).

19 **váru svá stór hǫgg hans:** 'so great were his blows' (nom. pl., see 12.3.3; 13.1).

20 **ekki vætta:** 'nothing at all'.

21 **aldri var svá til hans hǫggvit eða skotit:** 'he himself was never struck or shot' (*lit.* 'never was [it] thus to him struck or shot').

22 **yrði honum at meini:** 'caused him harm'; *yrdi*, 3sg. past subjunct. of *verða* 'become' (see 16.1).

____

____

____

____

____

VOCABULARY

annarr (*pl gen* annarra) *adj* other, another
áðr *conj* before
brynja (*pl nom/acc* -jur) *f* coat of mail
búa (býr; bjó, bjoggu; búinn) *vb* live (in a place), dwell; *refl* **búask** prepare (oneself); **búask til** prepare (oneself) for
býsk *3sg pres refl of* **búa**
dagr *m* day; **þann dag** on that day
drap (*inf* **drepa**) (he) killed
drepa (drepr; drap, drápu; drepinn) *vb* kill
engi (*n* ekki; *acc m* enga) *indef pron* no one, not one, no; (*n* **ekki**) nothing
fjǫldi *m* multitude
fylking (*pl nom/acc* -ar) *f* battle array, the ranks of an army
fyrir *prep* [*w acc*] before, instead of
gegnum (*also* **í gegnum**) *prep* [*w acc*] through
hitta (-tt-) *vb* meet; *refl* **hittask** meet one another
hjálmr (*pl acc* hjálma) *m* helmet
hjó *3sg past of* **hǫggva**
hlíf (*pl* -ar) *f* cover, protection (esp. of a shield or armor)
hǫgg (*pl nom/acc* hǫgg) *n* stroke, blow
hǫggva (høggr; hjó, hjoggu; hǫgg(v)inn) *vb* strike, hack, hew
lagði *3sg past of* **leggja**
lá (*inf* **liggja**) *vb* (it) lay
leggja (lagð-) *vb* lay, place; [*w dat*] stab, thrust
lengi *adv* long, a long time
liggja (liggr; lá, lágu, leginn) *vb* lie
lítill (*comp* minni) *adj* little, small
mein *n* hurt, harm; **verða [e-m] at meini** cause [sb] harm
miklu *adv* [*w comp*] much (*n dat sg of* **mikill**)
minni *comp adj* littler, smaller, less (*see* **lítill**)
neinn (*n* neitt) *indef pron* not one
neitt *n of* **neinn**
nema *conj* except
Randalín *f* Randalin (*personal name*)
rýrr *adj* thin
salr *m* hall
sár *n* wound
skilnaðr *m* parting
skjóta (skýtr; skaut, skutu; skotinn) *vb* shoot
skjǫldr (*pl acc* skjǫldu) *m* shield
skotit (*inf* **skjóta**) *ppart* shot
spjót *n* spear
standa (stendr; stóð, stóðu; staðinn) *vb* stand; **standa við** withstand
stórr (*pl nom/acc n* stór) *adj* big
taka (tekr; tók, tóku; tekinn) *vb* take; begin; *refl* **takask** begin, happen
tóksk *3sg past refl of* **taka**
vann (*inf* **vinna**) *vb* (he) won
vinna (vinnr; vann, unnu; unninn) *vb* win; **vinna at [e-m]** do away with, kill [sb]
vættr *f* creature, being; **ekki vætta** nothing at all
yrði *3sg past subjunct of* **verða**
þora (-ð-) *vb* dare

Lesson 12 Supplementary Exercises

1. Fill in the appropriate endings.

a. Sá mað__, sem var in__ mest__ bogmaðr, kom út frá in___ stór__ þing__.

b. Ek vil gef__ þér __ll in bezt__ l__nd (pl.).

c. __ll___ in___ hraust__st__ menn hljóp__ til in___ bezt__ skip__ (pl.).

d. Þeir Þorstein__ velj__ sér m__rg hvít hross.

2. Translate the sentences in exercise **1**.

a. ____

____

b. ____

c. ____

d. ____

____

3. Rewrite sentence **1.d** in the past tense.

____

4. The following sentences are from R.S. 12(1), but the words are in jumbled order. Put the words into their proper order, conjugating verbs to agree with their subjects and supplying the appropriate case forms of nouns and demonstrative pronouns. Hint: you may wish to refer back to the reading selection.

a. gefa / vera / ausa / vatna / nafn / ok / kalla / Ívarr/ sveinninn / ok

____

____

b. en / beinlauss / vera / sá / ok / bein / skylda / sveinn / sem / þar/ vera / brjósk / vera

____

____

c. Annar / Hvítserkr / inn / heita / þriði/ fjórði / Rǫgnvaldr / sonr / sá / inn / Bjǫrn

____

____

5. Translate the sentences in exercise **4.**

a. ____

____

b. ____

____

c. ____

____

6. Decline the masc. nouns *konungr* and *bogi* in the singular and plulral.

Sg *nom*	konungr	bogi
acc		
dat		
gen		
Pl *nom*		
acc		
dat		
gen		

7. Decline the neut. nouns *haf* and *hjarta* in the singular and plural.

Sg *nom*	haf	hjarta
acc		
dat		
gen		
Pl *nom*		
acc		
dat		
gen		

8. Decline the fem. nouns *bók* and *kona* in the singular and plural.

Sg *nom*	bók	kona
acc		
dat		
gen		
Pl *nom*		
acc		
dat		
gen		

9. Complete the declensions.

a. Masc.

	***sá* + Noun**	***þessi* + Noun**
Sg *nom*	sá maðr	____________
acc	____________	____________
dat	____________	____________
gen	____________	þessa vinar
Pl *nom*	____________	þessir vinir
acc	þá menn	____________
dat	____________	____________
gen	____________	____________

b. Fem.

	***sá* + Noun**	***þessi* + Noun**
Sg *nom*	sú ferð	____________
acc	____________	____________
dat	____________	____________
gen	____________	þessarar sǫgu
Pl *nom*	____________	____________
acc	þær ferðir	____________
dat	____________	þessum sǫgum
gen	____________	____________

c. Neut.

	***sá* + Noun**	***þessi* + Noun**
Sg *nom*	____________	____________
acc	þat ráð	____________
dat	____________	þessu barni
gen	____________	____________
Pl *nom*	____________	____________
acc	____________	____________
dat	____________	þessum bǫrnum
gen	þeira ráða	____________

10. Change the underlined nouns from singular to plural and make other necessary changes.

a. Kappi konungs fór með skip norðr af landinu.

____

b. Þetta barn fór með skútu til eyjarinnar.

____

c. Sú kona skýtr dýr ('animal', neut.) í þessum skógi.

____

d. Sá bogmaðr helt boga (dat.) ok skaut ǫru (dat.) at manni í krapparúminu.

____

____

11. Fill in the appropriate endings in the following passage drawn from *Heimskringla*.

Kringl___ heims_____ (def.), _____ (dem. pron.) er mannfólk_____ (def.) byggv___, er mjǫk vágskor____; ganga hǫf stór ór útsjá______ (def.) inn í jǫrð_____ (def.). Er ______ (dem. pron.) kunnigt, at haf g___ng___ frá Nǫrvasund_____ (pl.) ok alt út til Jórsalaland___.

Lesson 13 Supplementary Exercises

1. Fill in the appropriate endings.

a. Bjǫrn fór í þann tíma til nábú_____ (sg. def.) Skalla-Grím___.

b. In___ v___sk___ heimamenn bár___ sterk spjót (pl.).

2. Translate the sentences in exercise **1**.

a. ______________________________

____

b. ______________________________

3. Rewrite sentence **1.b**, making both noun phrases singular.

____

4. Change the underlined nouns from singular to plural and make other necessary changes.

a. Aðils konungr átti inn bezta hest í þann tíma.

____

b. Þá er Hrafnkell hafði land numit, þá efldi hann blót mikit ok lét gera hof mikit.

____

____

c. Heimamaðr Skalla-Gríms var sterkastr at afli þeira, er til váru, ok var inn grimmasti kappi.

____

____

d. Er sá víkingr var búinn, þá sigldi hann í ey nọkkur, sem var stór ok mjọk vágskorin.

____

____

5. Give the appropriate form of the noun in parentheses based on the given form of *annarr*.

Ex.: annarr sonr (sonr)

a. annarri ________ (saga)

b. ọðru ________ (sverð)

c. annarrar ________ (bók)

d. annat ________ (skip)

e. ọnnur ________ (kona)

f. ọðrum ________ (mál)

g. aðra ________ (fọr)

h. aðra ________ (knọrr)

i. annan ________ (bogi)

j. annars ________ (maðr)

6. Decline the following adjectives in all three genders, singular and plural, strong and weak.

a. *ungr* 'young'

	Strong			Weak		
	Masc	**Fem**	**Neut**	**Masc**	**Fem**	**Neut**
Sg *nom*	ungr	ung	ungt	ungi	unga	unga
acc						
dat						
gen						
Pl *nom*						
acc						
dat						
gen						

b. *góðr* 'good'

	Strong			Weak		
	Masc	**Fem**	**Neut**	**Masc**	**Fem**	**Neut**
Sg *nom*	góðr	góð	gott	góði	góða	góða
acc						
dat						
gen						
Pl *nom*						
acc						
dat						
gen						

c. *vænn* 'fine, handsome'

	Strong			Weak		
	Masc	**Fem**	**Neut**	**Masc**	**Fem**	**Neut**
Sg *nom*	vænn	væn	vænt	væni	væna	væna
acc						
dat						
gen						
Pl *nom*						
acc						
dat						
gen						

d. *mikill* 'great'

	Strong			Weak		
	Masc	**Fem**	**Neut**	**Masc**	**Fem**	**Neut**
Sg *nom*	mikill	mikil	mikit	mikli	mikla	mikla
acc						
dat						
gen						
Pl *nom*						
acc						
dat						
gen						

7. Change the following noun phrases from indefinite to definite (f.ex., change 'a good man' to 'the good man'). Also state the case and number of each noun phrase.

a. góðr maðr ______

b. stóran bekk ______

c. fegrst land ______

d. sterkar konur ______

e. veikar ǫrvar ______

f. ungri meyju ______

g. sigrsælum fóstrum ______

h. miklum veizlum ______

i. mestrar skútu ______

j. ágætra konunga ______

8. Change the following noun phrases from definite to indefinite, and state the case and number.

a. inn hvíti skjǫldr ____________________

b. inn hvíti bogi ____________________

c. ina hvítu boga ____________________

d. ina íslenzku skútu ____________________

e. in hvítu skip ____________________

f. inu íslenzka sverði ____________________

g. inum mestrum fegrðum ____________________

h. ins fagra hárs ____________________

i. ins fagra sumars ____________________

j. inna beztu ætta ____________________

9. Complete the following declensions.

a. Sg. nom. sá vinsæli maðr
acc. ____________________
dat. ____________________
gen. ____________________
Pl. nom. ____________________
acc. þá vinsælu menn
dat. ____________________
gen. ____________________

b. Sg. nom. sú langa ferð
acc. ____________________
dat. ____________________
gen. ____________________
Pl. nom. ____________________
acc. þær lǫngu ferðir
dat. ____________________
gen. ____________________

c. Sg. nom. ____________________
acc. þat illa ráð
dat. ____________________
gen. ____________________
Pl. nom. ____________________
acc. ____________________
dat. ____________________
gen. þeira illu ráða

10. Word search. Find the Old Icelandic words and translate them into English.

I N H V B R I K U F Y R R H E
S N E M M A S L G L E G G J A
O S R Y M M R E S A L D Á O J
I Ǫ I F T B U N Y F L Á B S P
N F X G H A E N Á A Z F R A M
N O Ǫ V L R H R U R T R G H S
L J E J B A R L G K R S M A K
E P N M A V A A S O H N A M I
N I A F N E U G N S A E R R P
Z V G R N L S A E T F M G A A
K E H A A J T B R R L M R M K
R S Z E X A R R I Z B A J M O
F T F J Y V Z O S F Á R P R S
K R K N Ǫ R R T K E Ǫ Z O T T
K E U L Á G A G N A F J Y T R

afarkostr ________
____
afl ________
aptr ________
banna ________
barn ________
berg ________
brot ________
eiga ________
ellztr ________
fár ________

fram ________
fyrr ________
gagn ________
hamrammr ________
____
heyra ________
hraustr ________
innlenzkr ________
knǫrr ________
lagabrot ________
____

leggja ________
margr ________
munu ________
neyta ________
sigla ________
skipakostr ________
____
snemma ________
snerisk ________
velja ________
vestr ________

Ór *Ragnars sǫgu loðbrókar* (15. kap.)
(From the *Saga of Ragnar Lodbrok*, Chap. 15)

3. The Battle Turns against Ragnar

En þó lauk svá bardaga þeira, at allt lið Ragnars fell, en at honum váru bornir skildir ok svá handtekinn.[23] Nú var hann spurðr, hvat manna hann var,[24] en hann þagði við[25] ok svaraði engu.

Þá mælti Ella konungr: "Sjá[26] maðr mun verða at koma í meiri mannraun, ef hann vill eigi segja oss, hverr hann er. Nú skal kasta honum[27] í einn ormgarð ok láta hann þar sitja mjǫk lengi, ok ef hann mælir nakkvat þat, er vér megim skilja,[28] at hann sé[29] Ragnarr, þá skal hann í brott taka[30] sem skjótast." Nú er honum þangat fylgt,[31] ok hann sitr þar mjǫk lengi, svá at hvergi festask ormar við hann.

Þá mæltu menn: "Þessi maðr er mikill fyrir sér;[32] hann bitu eigi vápn í dag, en nú granda honum eigi ormar."

Þá mælti Ella konungr, at hann væri flettr af klæði því, er hann hafði yzt, ok nú var svá gert, ok hengu ormar ǫllum megin á honum.

Translate: ____

____

____

____

____

____

____

____

____

____

---

23 **at honum váru bornir skildir ok svá handtekinn:** 'he was overborne by shields and so was captured' (*lit.* 'at him were borne shields and so [he was] seized'); *skildir*, nom. pl. of *skjǫldr* 'shield' (see 17.6).

24 **hvat manna hann var:** 'what sort of man (*lit.* what of men) he was'.

25 **hann þagði við:** 'he kept silent'.

26 **sjá = þessi** 'this' (see 12.1).

27 **skal kasta honum:** 'he shall be cast' (*lit.* 'shall cast him').

28 **þat, er vér megim skilja:** 'that [by] which we may discern'; *megim*, 1pl. pres. subjunct. of *mega* 'be able' (see 15.5).

29 **at hann sé:** 'that he is'; *sé*, 3sg. pres. subjunct. of *vera* 'be' (see 16.2).

30 **skal hann í brott taka:** 'he shall be taken away' (lit. 'shall take him away').

31 **er honum þangat fylgt:** 'he was (*lit.* '[it] was to him) brought there'.

32 **mikill fyrir sér:** 'strong, powerful, mighty'.

VOCABULARY

bera (berr; bar, báru; borinn) *vb* carry, bear
bitu (*inf* **bíta**) *vb* (they) bit
bíta (bítr; beit, bitu; bitinn) *vb* bite
bornir (*inf* **bera**) *ppart* borne, carried (*m nom pl*)
dagr *m* day; **í dag** today
einn *adj* one, a certain
engi *indef pron* no, not one; (*n*) nothing
engu *n dat sg of* **engi**
festa (-st-) *vb* fasten, fix; *refl* **festask** fasten (oneself)
fletta (-tt-) *vb* strip
flettr (*inf* **fletta**) *ppart* stripped (*m nom sg*)
fylgja (-d/ð-) *vb* [*w dat*] follow, accompany; help, side with, go with
fylgt (*inf* **fylgja**) *ppart* brought
gera (-ð-) *vb* make, do
gert (*inf* **gera**) *ppart* done
granda (-að-) *vb* [*w dat*] injure
handtekinn *adj* taken by hand, taken alive
hanga (hengr/hangir; hékk, hengu/héngu, hanginn) *vb* hang
hengu (*inf* **hanga**) *vb* (they) hung
hvergi *adv* nowhere
lauk (*inf* **lúka**) *vb* ended
lengi *adv* long, a long time
lúka (lýkr; lauk, luku; lokinn) *vb* [*w dat*] end, finish
mannraun *f* trial (of courage), danger, peril; adversity
mega (má, megu; mátti; mátt) *vb* be able, be allowed
megim (*inf* **mega**) *vb* (we) may (*1pl pres subjunct*)
megin *adv* on the side; **ǫllum megin** on all sides
meiri *comp adj* greater (*see* **mikill**)
mikill *adj* big, great; **mikill fyrir sér** strong, powerful, mighty
nakkvat *var of* **nǫkkut** (*see* **nǫkkurr**)
nǫkkurr (*n* nǫkkut) *indef pron* any; (*n*) anything
ormgarðr *m* snake-pit
oss *pron* us (*acc/dat of* **vér**)
sem *conj* as; [*w superl*] as ... as possible; **sem skjótast** at once, as soon as possible
sé (*inf* **vera**) *vb* is, may be (*3sg pres subjuct*)
sjá (= **þessi**) *dem pron/adj* this (one)
skilja (-d-) *vb* discern, understand
skildir *nom pl of* **skjǫldr**
skjótast *superl adv* most quickly; soonest (*see* **skjótt**); **sem skjótast** at once, as soon as possible
skjótt *adv* swiftly, quickly; soon
skjǫldr (*pl nom* skildir) *m* shield
spurðr (*inf* **spyrja**) *ppart* asked
spyrja (spurð-) *vb* ask
svara (-að-) *vb* [*w dat*] answer, reply
verða (verðr; varð, urðu; orðinn) *vb* become; **verða at** [*w inf*] must, need to, be obliged to [do sth]
vér *pron* we
yztr *superl adj* outermost
þagði (*inf* **þegja**) *vb* (he) was silent
þangat *adv* (to) there, thither
þegja (þagð-) *vb* be silent; **þegja við** remain silent

Lesson 14 Supplementary Exercises

1. Fill in the appropriate endings.

a. Þeir ber__ sverð___ (pl. def.) til þing__.

b. Þeir stand__ upp af in___ óœðr__ bekk.

c. Skip___ (pl. def.) er__ hér á Ísland__.

d. Þeir segj__ frá á____ (def.) í sǫg_____ (def.).

e. Þeir Bjǫrn gang__ austr til á__ (indef.).

f. Þeir tak__ menn____ (pl. def.) með sér.

g. Þorgrím__ ok Óláf__ setj__ stól____ (pl. def.) úti hjá búð_____ (def.).

h. Þeir Egil__ vit__, hvar spjót___ (pl. def.) væri.

2. Rewrite the sentences from exercise **1** in the past tense.

a. ______________________________

b. ______________________________

c. ______________________________

d. ______________________________

e. ______________________________

f. ______________________________

g. ______________________________

h. ______________________________

3. Rewrite your answers to exercise **2**, changing the subject of each sentence from pl. to sing. and making other necessary changes.

a. ______________________________

b. ______________________________

c. ______________________________

d. ______________________________

e. ______________________________

f. ______________________________

g. ______________________________

h. ______________________________

4. Decline the first four numerals.[33]

	einn 'one'			tveir 'two'		
	Masc	**Fem**	**Neut**	**Masc**	**Fem**	**Neut**
nom	einn	ein	eitt	tveir	tvær	tvau
acc						
dat						
gen						

	þrír 'three'			fjórir 'four'		
	Masc	**Fem**	**Neut**	**Masc**	**Fem**	**Neut**
nom	þrír	þrjár	þrjú	fjórir	fjórar	fjǫgur
acc						
dat						
gen						

5. Provide the appropriate form of the numeral in parentheses.

a. Son átti sér (einn) einn, er Þorsteinn er nefndr.

b. Hann hafði með sér skip (tveir) ________, full af gulli ok silfri.

c. Hestr Njáls var (fjórir) ________ vetra gamall.

d. Gunnarr reið í brott (tveir) ________ nóttum síðar ok (tveir) ________ menn með honum.

e. Einarr dró bogann ok brast þá boginn í (tveir) ________ hluti.

f. Þat er grimmast allra dýra sem ganga á (fjórir) ________ fótum.

6. Translate the sentences in exercise **5**.

a. ________

b. ________

c. ________

d. ________

____

e. ________

____

f. ________

____

7. Translate into Old Icelandic.

Ex.: the kings (nom. pl.) konungarnir

a. the vikings (acc. pl.) ________

b. to the swords (dat. pl.) ________

[33] The numerals remain virtually unchanged in Modern Icelandic, evidence of the strong retention of form between the Old and Modern Icelandic.

c. to the bows (dat. pl.) ________________

d. the women (nom. pl.) ________________

e. of the chieftains (gen. pl.) ________________

f. the books (acc. pl.) ________________

g. to the rivers (dat. pl.) ________________

h. of the sagas (gen. pl.) ________________

i. the eyes (acc. pl.) ________________

j. of the lands (gen. pl.) ________________

8. Supply the appropriate word for 'his':

a. Einarr dró boga ______.

b. Elfráðr inn ríki réð fyrir landi ________.

c. Ek vil þiggja systur ______.

d. Egill gekk til nábúa ______, ok tók heimanann ______.

9. Change the underlined nouns from singular to plural and make other necessary changes.

a. <u>Sonr</u> Sigurðar var mikill vexti, vænn yfirlits ok vel viti borinn.

____

____

b. <u>Barn</u> Egils var mannvænt, frítt sýnum ok vel viti borit.

____

____

10. Write the 1st, 2nd, and 3rd person sing. pres. forms of the following verbs.

Weak verbs

kasta (-að-):	ek __________	þú __________	hann __________
hlýða (-dd-):	ek __________	þú __________	hann __________
lýsa (-t-):	ek __________	þú __________	hann __________

Weak verbs with vowel shift

berja (barð-):	ek __________	þú __________	hann __________
hyggja (hugð-)	ek __________	þú __________	hann __________
mylja (muld-)	ek __________	þú __________	hann __________

Strong verbs

drepa:	ek __________	þú __________	hann __________
ráða:	ek __________	þú __________	hann __________
sjóða:	ek __________	þú __________	hann __________

11. Fill in the appropriate endings and missing vowels in the following passage from *Ragnars saga loðbrókar.*

Nú h__ld__ Ragnar__ skip____ sín____ (pl.) til England_, sem hann hafð__ ætla__. Hon____ gaf byr__ hvass__ (pl.), svá at við England br__t__ (pres.) hann báða knǫrr__ sín__ (pl.), en á land komsk all__ lið hans, ok held__ (pl.) klæð____ sín____ (pl.) ok vápn____ (pl.). Ok þar, sem hann k__m__ (pres.) við þorp ok borg___ (pl.) ok kastal__ (pl.), þá vinn__ hann. En konung__ sá hét Ella, er þá réð Englandi. Hann hafð__ haf__ frétt____ (pl.) til Ragnar__, er hann fór ór land__.

Lesson 15 Supplementary Exercises

1. Fill in the appropriate endings and missing vowels.

a. Þat er mæl__, at fá___ menn mun__ vita all___ h__fn___ í Sólund____ (pl.).

b. Bjǫrn ok Hvítserkr bár__ Ívar á st__ng____, því at hann mátt__ eigi g__ng__.

c. Ǫnund__ svarað__: "Ek e___ feg____ orð____, Egill, er þú er__ kom____."

d. Þat mun ljós__ verð__, hvárt þú mæl___ þe____ af alv__r__ eða hégóm__.

e. Sýn__sk mér þat ráð, meðan vit er____ á líf__, at vit t__k____ mál þe____ undir okk__ ok s__t____ niðr.

2. The seven most common preterite-present verbs.

a. Conjugate the three modal auxiliary verbs in the present tense: *mega* 'be able to, may', *munu* 'will, shall (*futurity*)', and *skulu* 'shall (*necessity*), must'.

	mega	**munu**	**skulu**
1sg	__________	__________	__________
2sg	__________	__________	__________
3sg	__________	__________	__________
1pl	__________	__________	__________
2pl	__________	__________	__________
3pl	__________	__________	__________

b. Conjugate the following non-modal auxiliary preterite-present verbs in the present tense: *eiga* 'own, be married to'; *kunna* 'know, be able'; *muna* 'remember'; *vita* 'know'; and *þurfa* 'need'.

	eiga	**kunna**	**muna**	**vita**	**þurfa**
1sg	______	______	______	______	______
2sg	______	______	______	______	______
3sg	______	______	______	______	______
1pl	______	______	______	______	______
2pl	______	______	______	______	______
3pl	______	______	______	______	______

c. Conjugate the seven most common preterite-present verbs (above) in the past tense.

	mega	**munu**	**skulu**	**eiga**
1sg	______	______	______	______
2sg	______	______	______	______
3sg	______	______	______	______
1pl	______	______	______	______
2pl	______	______	______	______
3pl	______	______	______	______

	kunna	**muna**	**vita**	**þurfa**
1sg	______	______	______	______
2sg	______	______	______	______
3sg	______	______	______	______
1pl	______	______	______	______
2pl	______	______	______	______
3pl	______	______	______	______

3. Supply the appropriate form of *vera* in the pres. tense.

a. Nú mælir konungr við dóttur sína: "Þú ___ert___ vitr kona."

b. Helgi svarar: "Hvat ______ þat, konungsdóttir?"

c. Vér ________ átta saman," segja þeir.

d. Maðr kemr mikill ok fagr með eitt auga ok mælir: "Eigi ________ þér góðir menn."

e. Þeir brœðr, synir Skíða, _______ góðir menn allir.

f. Þrándr segir: "Ek ______ vápnaðr ('armed') betr en þú."

4. Rewrite the sentences from exercise **3** in the past tense.

a. ____

____

b. ____

c. ____

d. ____

____

e. ____

f. ____

5. Translate the sentences in exercise **4**.

a. ____

____

b. ____

c. ____

d. ____

____

e. ____

f. ____

6. Rewrite the verbs in the pres. subjunctive.

a. hun segir	at hun *segi*
b. þér gerið	at þér __________
c. hann ferr	at hann __________
d. vér sendum	at vér __________
e. þú kastar	at þú __________
f. ek skýt	at ek __________
g. þeir heita	at þeir __________

7. Complete the following declensions.

a.	Sg. nom.	þessi vinsæli maðr
	acc.	__________________
	dat.	__________________
	gen.	__________________
	Pl. nom.	__________________
	acc.	þessa vinsælu menn
	dat.	__________________
	gen.	__________________

b.	Sg. nom.		þessi stóra kona
		acc.	______________________________
		dat.	______________________________
		gen.	______________________________
	Pl. nom.		______________________________
		acc.	þessar stóru konur
		dat.	______________________________
		gen.	______________________________
c.	Sg. nom.		______________________________
		acc.	þetta illa ráð
		dat.	______________________________
		gen.	______________________________
	Pl. nom.		______________________________
		acc.	______________________________
		dat.	______________________________
		gen.	þessara illu ráða

8. Match each Old Icelandic word with its English meaning by drawing a line between them.

draga	between
feginn	draw
ljóss	insincerity
milli	earnestness
nær	located
hégómi	happy
alvara	near
staddr	clear

9. Fill in the appropriate endings and missing vowels.

Síðan st__ð Egil__ upp ok mælt__ hátt: “Hvárt er Ǫnund__ sjón__ hér í þingbrekku_____ (def.)?”

Ǫnund__ kv__zk þar ver__, – “ek em fegin__ orð_____, Egil__, er þú er__ kom_____; m__n þat all__ bœt__ til um þat, er hér st__nd__ milli mál__ (sing.) mann__ (pl.).”

“Hvárt r__ð__ (pres.) þú því, er Steinar__, son__ þin__, sœk___ s__kum Þorstein, son min__, ok h__fi__ dreg___ saman fjǫlmenni, til þ_____ at ger__ at Þorstein urðarmanni?”

"Því v__ld ek eigi," seg__ Ǫnund__, "er þeir er__ ósátt___, h__fi ek þar lag__ til m__rg orð ok b__ð___ (ppart.) Steinar sætt__sk við Þorstein."

10. Give the English equivalents of the following Old Norse place names. (Hint: compare the map on pp. x–xi with the map on pp. 48–49 of the textbook.)

Grœnland ______________
Vestribyggð ____________________
Eystribyggð ____________________
Hvarf ___________________
Vínland ___________________
Ísland ___________
Færeyjar ____________

Hjaltland ______________
Orkneyjar _____________
Suðreyjar ____________
Írland ___________
Nóregr ___________
Svíþjóð ___________
Danmǫrk ___________

Ór *Ragnars sǫgu loðbrókar* (15. kap.)

(From the *Saga of Ragnar Lodbrok*, Chap. 15)

4. Ragnar in the Snake Pit Calls to His Piglets

Þá mælti Ragnarr: "Gnyðja mundu nú grísir, ef þeir vissi, hvat inn gamli þyldi."[34] Ok þótt hann mælti slíkt, þá vissu þeir eigi at gørr, at Ragnarr væri þat heldr en annarr konungr. Nú kvað hann vísu:

Translate: ____

____

____

____

____

Orrostur hefk[35] áttar,[36] ______________________
þærs[37] ágætar þóttu, ______________________

[34] **ef þeir vissi, hvat inn gamli þyldi:** 'if they knew what the old one was suffering'; *vissi*, 3pl. past subjunct. of *vita* 'know'; *þyldi*, 3pl. past subjunct. of *þola* 'suffer' (see 16.1).

[35] **hefk** = **hef** + **ek:** 'I have'.

[36] **Orrostur hefk áttar:** 'Battles have I had'; *áttar* (ppart. of *eiga* 'own, have', fem. acc. pl.) modifies *orrostur*, so *orrostur ... áttar* is, literally, 'owned battles'.

[37] **þærs** = **þær** + **es** = **þær er:** 'those (fem.) which'.

gerða ek mǫrgum mǫnnum
mein, fimm tigu ok eina;[38]
eigi hugðak[39] orma
at aldrlagi mínu;
verðr mjǫk mǫrgu sinni[40],
þats[41] minnst varir sjálfan.[42]

Ok enn kvað hann:

Gnyðja mundu grísir,
ef galtar hag vissi,
mér er gnótt at grandi,
grafa inn rǫnum sínum
ok harðliga hváta,
hafa mik sogit, ormar;[43]
nú munk[44] nár[45] af bragði
ok nær dýrum deyja.

Nú lætr hann líf sitt, ok er hann nú fœrðr á brott þaðan.

En synir Ragnars hǫfðu herjat of Suðrríki. Þá sneru þeir á Norðrlǫnd ok ætluðu at vitja ríkis síns, þess er Ragnarr réð fyrir. En þeir vissu eigi herfǫr hans, hversu hon hafði orðit, ok þó er þeim mikil forvitni[46] á, hversu hon hafði orðit.

[38] **fimm tigu ok eina:** 'fifty-one', refers to **orrostur** in the first line.
[39] **hugðak = hugða + ek:** 'I thought'.
[40] **mjǫk mǫrgu sinni:** 'on very many occasions' (*lit.* 'very many a time').
[41] **þats = þat + es = þat er:** 'that which'.
[42] **þats minnst varir sjálfan:** 'that which [one] oneself least expects'; *varir*, 3sg. pres. of *vara* 'give (one) a foreboding of'.
[43] **ormar:** 'snakes', the subject of the three preceding verbs, **grafa**. **hváta**, and **hafa**.
[44] **munk = mun + ek:** 'I will'.
[45] **munk nár:** 'I will [be] a corpse'.
[46] **er þeim mikil forvitni:** 'they are greatly curious' (*lit.* '[there] is to them great curiosity').

VOCABULARY

aldrlag *n* fate, destiny; end of life
áttar (*inf* **eiga**) *ppart* had (*f acc pl*)
bragð *n* sudden, brisk movement; moment; **af bragði** at once
deyja (deyr; dó, dóu; dáinn) *vb* die
dýr *n* animal, beast
eiga (á, eigu; átti; áttr) *vb* own, have
enn *adv* still, yet; further, moreover
forvitni *f* curiosity
fœra (-ð-) *vb* bring, convey
fœrðr (*inf* **fœra**) *ppart* carried
galtar *gen sg of* **gǫltr**
gamall *adj* old
gamli (*gen* -a) *m* old one (*nickname*) (*wk m nom sg of* **gamall**)
gnótt *f* abundance
gnyðja (gnudd-) *vb* grunt
grafa (grefr; gróf, grófu, grafinn) *vb* dig
grand *n* injury
gríss (*pl* -ir) *m* young pig
gǫltr (*gen* galtar) *m* boar, hog
gørr *comp adv* more fully, clearly; **at gørr** for certain
hagr *m* state, condition
harðliga *adv* forcibly, harshly, severe-ly; hard
heldr (*superl* helzt) *comp adv* more, very, rather
herfǫr *f* military expedition
herja (-að-) *vb* raid, harry; ravage, plunder
hugða (*inf* **hyggja**) *vb* (I) thought
hváta *vb* stick (in), poke, pierce
hyggja (hugð-) *vb* think; **hyggja at** consider
láta (lætr; lét, létu; látinn) *vb* let; lose; **láta lífit** lose one's life
lætr (*inf* **láta**) *vb* loses
margr *adj* [*w sg*] many a (in collective sense)
minnst *superl adv* least
nár *m* corpse, dead man
Norðrlǫnd *n pl* Northern Lands (Northern Europe) (*place name*)
rani *m* snout
rǫnum *dat pl of* **rani**
sinn *n* a time, occasion; **mǫrgu sinni** many a time, on many occasions
sneru (*inf* **snúa**) *vb* (they) turned
snúa (snýr; snøri/sneri; snúinn) *vb* turn
sogit (*inf* **súga**) *ppart* sucked
Suðrríki *n* Southern Realm (Southern Europe) (*place name*)
súga (sýgr; saug/só, sugum; soginn) *vb* suck
vara (-ð-) *vb* give (one) a foreboding of; **þat varir [e-n]** [sb] has a presentiment
vera (er; var, váru; verit) *vb* be; **er [e-m] [e-t]** [sb] has [sth]
vissi (*inf* **vita**) *vb* (they) knew (*3pl past subjunct*)
vissu (*inf* **vita**) *vb* (they) knew
vita (veit, vitu; vissi; vitaðr) *vb* know
vitja (-að-) *vb* [*w gen*] visit
vísa *f* verse
þaðan *adv* from there, thence
þola (-d-) *vb* suffer, endure
þóttu (*inf* **þykkja**) *vb* (they) seemed
þykkja (þótt-) *vb* [*w dat*] seem (*impers*); *refl* **þykkjask** seem to one, consider oneself; **þykkjask vita** feel convinced
þyldi (*inf* **þola**) *vb* suffered (*3pl past subjunct*)
ætla (-að-) *vb* think, intend

Lesson 16 Supplementary Exercises

1. Fill in the appropriate endings and missing vowels.

a. "Ek man þá dag__," seg___ Egill, "at hvár____tveggja okkr____ mund__ þykkja þat ólíklig__." (Hint: *þykkja* takes the dative.)

b. Bjarni spurð__, hvar Þórðr v__r__ (past subjunct.), ok menn sv__r__ð__, at hann m__nd__ (past subjunct.) til hrossa farinn vera.

c. Ek mun ganga inn til f__ð__r þ__n__ ('your father') ok segja h__n____ slíkt, sem ek vil.

d. Ok því at þér vil___ eigi hlýða m__n__ ráði, þá skul___ þér enga ván eiga m__n____ fylgðar. (*fylgð* fem. 'help, support')

2. Fill in the chart with the subjunctive of *vera*.

Pres *1sg*	__________	***Past*** *1sg*	__________
2sg	__________	*2sg*	__________
3sg	__________	*3sg*	__________
1pl	__________	*1pl*	__________
2pl	__________	*2pl*	__________
3pl	__________	*3pl*	__________

3. Supply the appropriate subjunctive form of *vera*.

a. Konungr tekr Gunnlaugi vel ok spyrr, hverr hann ____ (pres.).

b. Konungr tók Gunnlaugi vel ok spurði, hverr hann ______ (past).

c. Hrafn segir, at þeir Gunnlaugr ok brœðr sínir ____ (pres.) innar beztu ættar.

d. Hrafn sagði, at þeir Gunnlaugr ok brœðr sínir ______ (past) innar beztu ættar.

4. Decline the 1st and 2nd person dual pronouns.

	1st		**2nd**	
Dual *nom*	__________	'we'	__________	'you'
acc	__________	'us'	__________	'you'
dat	__________	'(to) us'	__________	'(to) you'
gen	__________	'of us'	__________	'of you'

5. Supply the appropriate form of the 1st or 2nd person dual pronoun in the following sentences adapted from various sagas.

a. Hárekr segir: "Síðan kom þar Þórólfr með hundrað ('a hundred') manna ok ætlaði at drepa _okkr_ brœðr ok alla þá menn, er ________ fylgðu." (*Egils saga Skalla-Grímssonar*)

b. Bergþóra segir: "Ek var ung gefin Njáli, ok hefi ek því heitit honum, at eitt ('the same thing') skyldi ganga yfir ('befall') ________ bæði." (*Njáls saga*)

c. Njáll mælti: "Hvat skulum ________ nú til ráða ('plans', neut. gen. pl.) taka?" (*Njáls saga*)

d. Ek sagða svá, sem mér var í hug ('was in my mind'), at ek mynda aldri ganga á hǫnd ('go into service, become a retainer') Haraldi konungi ok svá myndið ________ gera báðir. (*Egils saga*)

e. Ek ætla mér vera góðan kost ('choice'), hvárr sem ('which ever') upp kemr ('happens'), ef _______ Þorsteinn skulum reyna með ('put to the test') ________. (*Egils saga*)

f. Þat er vel, at _______ reynið með ________, hvárr frœknari er. (*Þorsteins saga Víkingssonar*)

6. Translate the sentences in exercise **5.**

a. ______________________________

____

____

b. ______________________________

____

____

c. ______________________________

d. ______________________________

____

____

e. ______________________________

____

f. ______________________________

7. Decline the following phrases.

	my king	my story	my land
Sg nom	konungr minn	saga mín	land mitt
acc			
dat			
gen			

Pl *nom*			
acc			
dat			
gen			

	your (sg.) bow	**your (sg.) book**	**your (sg.) word**
Sg *nom*	bogi þinn	bók þín	orð þitt
acc			
dat			
gen			
Pl *nom*			
acc			
dat			
gen			

8. Decline the 1st person dual possessive adjective *okkarr*. (Note that the 2nd person dual *ykkarr* and the 1st and 2nd person pl. *várr* and *yð(v)arr* decline similarly.)

	Masc	**Fem**	**Neut**
Sg *nom*			
acc			
dat			
gen			
Pl *nom*			
acc			
dat			
gen			

9. The following sentences are taken from R.S. 16. Fill in the blanks with the appropriate phrase from the box, conjugating the verbs as necessary.

~~at ǫllu~~	finnask á	gera gaman	geta til
hafa farizk	komask undan	kveða á	

Ex: Gunnarr svarar: "Litlar sǫgur megu ganga frá hesti mínum; hann er ungr ok óreyndr __at ǫllu__."

a. "Hildigunnr _______ þess _______," segja þeir, "at þú myndir góðr af hestinum."

b. Ríða þeir þá heim. Spurði Starkaðr at, hversu þeim ___________ ___________.

c. Þeir sǫgðu, at Gunnarr gerði góða ferð þeira; - "hann hét at etja hesti sínum, ok __________ vér _____, nær þat hestavíg skyldi vera."

d. "Þat mun opt _______________," segir Hildigunnr, "at Gunnarr er seinþreyttr til vandræða, en harðdrœgr, ef hann má eigi ____________________."

10. Write the 3 sing. and 1 pl. pres. subjunct. and past subjunct. forms of the following verbs:

Weak verbs		**Present**	**Past**
kasta (-að-):	hann	________________	________________
	vér	________________	________________
flytja (flutt-):	hon	________________	________________
	vér	________________	________________
kveðja (kvadd-):	hon	________________	________________
	vér	________________	________________
setja (-tt-):	hann	________________	________________
	vér	________________	________________

Strong verbs		**Present**	**Past**
aka (*3 pl. past* óku):	hann	________________	________________
	vér	________________	________________
frjósa (*3 pl. past* frusu):	þat	________________	________________
	vér	________________	________________
gefa (*3 pl. past* gáfu):	hon	________________	________________
	vér	________________	________________
ráða (*3 pl. past* réðu):	hann	________________	________________
	vér	________________	________________

11. Examples of 3 sing. past subjunctive forms are provided. Working from the subjunctive back to the indicative, supply the 3 sing. past indic., 3 pl. past indic., and inf. forms of each verb.

Weak verbs	3sg Past Indic.	3pl. Past Indic.	Inf.
þat berði:	þat ____________,	þau ____________,	at ____________
hon segði:	hon ____________,	þær ____________,	at ____________
hann spyrði:	hann ____________,	þeir ____________,	at ____________
hon vekti:	hon ____________,	þær ____________,	at ____________

Strong verbs

hon bæri:	hon ___________,	þær ___________,	at ___________
hann dræpi:	hann ___________,	þeir ___________,	at ___________
þat fœri:	þat ___________,	þau ___________,	at ___________
hon heldi:	hon ___________,	þær ___________,	at ___________
hann skyti	hann ___________,	þeir ___________,	at ___________
hann sæti:	hann ___________,	þeir ___________,	at ___________

Lesson 17 Supplementary Exercises

1. Translate into Old Icelandic:

a. The eagle flies from (*ór* + dat.) his hand.

____

b. He takes (his) hand from (*frá* + dat.) the eagle.

____

2. Provide the comparative and superlative forms of the irregular adjectives and adverbs.

Positive form	Comparative	Superlative
illr	___________	___________
illa	___________	___________
litill	___________	___________
litt	___________	___________
vel	___________	___________

3. Decline the comparative adjective *bjartari* in the singular and plural.

	Masc	**Fem**	**Neut**
Sg *nom*	___________	___________	___________
acc	___________	___________	___________
dat	___________	___________	___________
gen	___________	___________	___________
Pl *nom*	___________	___________	___________
acc	___________	___________	___________
dat	___________	___________	___________
gen	___________	___________	___________

4. Supply the present participle of the verb given in parentheses, paying attention to case and gender. Then translate the phrase.

Ex.: *sofandi* (sofa) konungr — *a sleeping king*

a. inna __________ (skína) sverða __________

b. __________ (ganga) konum __________

c. it __________ (fara) skip __________

d. __________ (brenna 'burn') mann __________

5. Supply the preterite infinitive (see 17.5) of the verb in parentheses in the following sentences.

a. Hann kvazk *mundu* (munu) í Ísland koma.

b. Ek hugða þik __________ (munu) láta hann fara.

c. Þeir báðu hann hrossanna leita __________ (skulu).

d. Ek hugða konunginn __________ (vilja) minn faðir drepa.

6. Translate the sentences in exercise **5.**

a. *He said he would come to Iceland.*

b. __________

c. __________

d. __________

7. Decline the masculine nouns *kǫttr* 'cat', *knǫrr* 'ship', *lǫgr* 'sea', and *hjǫrtr* 'deer' in the singular and plural. (Hint: the *-rr* of *knǫ**rr*** belongs to the stem.)

Sg *nom*	*kǫttr*	*knǫrr*	*lǫgr*	*hjǫrtr*
acc				
dat				
gen				
Pl *nom*				
acc				
dat				
gen				

8. Fill in the appropriate endings and missing vowels in the following passage from *Ragnars saga loðbrókar.*

En s__n___ (pl.) Ragnar__ h__fð__ herj__ of Suðrríki. Þá sn__r__ þeir á Norðrlǫnd ok ætl__ð__ at vitj__ ríkis s__n__, þess er Ragnar__ réð fyrir. En þeir viss__ eigi herfǫr hans, hversu hon hafð__ orð___, ok þó er þeim mikil forvitn__ á, hversu hon hafð__ orð___.

9. Fill in the appropriate endings.[47]

Skaði, dótt___ Þjaza jǫtun__, tók silfr___ (def.) ok fer__ til Ásgerð__ at hefn__ ('avenge', w. gen. obj.) fǫður sín__.

En Æs___ (pl. of Áss) buð__ henn__ sætt ('settlement, reconciliation', strong fem.), at hon skal kjós__ ('choose') sér mann af Ás___.

Þá sá hon ein__ mann. "Þe____ ('this', acc. sing. masc.) kýs ek," mælt__ hon. En þat var Njǫrðr.

Skað__ vild__ haf__ stað þ____ ('that', acc. sing. masc.), er fað___ henn___ hafð__ át__, þar sem heit___ Þrymheim___.

En Njǫrð__ vill ver__ nær haf__. Þá sagð__ hann, at þau skyldu ver__ stundum í Þrymheim__, stundum nær haf__.

Þá fór__ þau upp á fjallit ('the mountain') ok bygð__ saman í Þrymheim__. Ok fer__ Skað__ mjǫk með bog__ ok skýt__ dýr.

10. Translate the passage above.

---

[47] This passage is based on the account in the *Prose Edda* of the giant Þjazi, his daughter Skaði, and the god Njǫrðr, here called a man.

"Otter's Ransom" and "Fafnir, Regin, and Sigurd" Introduction

Skáldskaparmál is the name of the 'poetic diction' section of *The Prose Edda*. This section of this 13th-century Icelandic book contains a wealth of mythological stories. The two short stories given here concern the ancient tale of the magic ring and the great treasure taken from the dwarf Andvari. The first story, *Af otrgjǫldum* ('About Otter's Ransom'), gives the background leading to Loki's seizing the magic ring. Loki gives the ring to Odin who is forced to relinquish it to his host, the giant Hreidmar. The second story, *Frá Fafni, Regin, ok Sigurði* ('About Fafnir, Regin, and Sigurd') recounts how the ring and treasure passed into the possession of the young hero Sigurd.

Both parts of this account are also told in *The Saga of the Volsungs* (*Vǫlsunga saga*) and in a series of eddic poems about Sigurd and the Volsung family. Together, these different tales give a broad account of how the ring and treasure pass through the control of dwarves, giants, gods, and dragons, before coming into the hands of Sigurðr Fáfnisbani, the slayer of the dragon Fafnir.

The Present Tense in Narrative, a Characteristic of Old Norse Prose

At several points in these stories, the verb tenses change from past to present in the course of the storytelling. This changing of tenses is a characteristic of Old Icelandic narrative style and is found widely in the sagas and other works such as *The Prose Edda*. In the main, Icelandic prose is told in the past tense, but it is common for the narration to shift abruptly to the present, then return again to the past. Such alternations in tense, while natural to Old Icelandic storytelling, often do not flow well in English or other modern languages. The resulting awkwardness in modern translation is frequently smoothed out by rendering all verbs in the past tense.

The following examples illustrate some contexts in which this type of alternation occurs.

- **Introducing a Character's Name.** Sometimes a character is introduced in the present tense (for example, *er nefndr* or *heitir* 'is named'), even when the surrounding verbs are in the past tense. An example occurs in Section 1 of Otter's Ransom: the Æsir **came** (*kómu*, past tense) to a farmhouse and **went** in (*gengu*, past tense), and the farmer who **lived** there (*bjó*, past tense) **is** named Hreidmar (*er*, present tense).
- **Heightening the Dramatic Effect.** Recounting past events in the present tense is a narrative device called the "historical present,"

"dramatic present," or "narrative present". The device is used to heighten the dramatic effect of an action sequence. A good illustration is found in Section 2 of Otter's Ransom. When Hreidmar **saw** the Otter (*sá*, past tense), he **called** his sons (*kallaði*, past tense), and **says** to them (*segir*, present tense) what happened, and then they **attack** the Æsir (*ganga at*, present tense), **take** hold of them (*taka*, present tense), and **bind** them (*binda*, present tense).

- **Indirect Speech.** In indirect speech, verbs can appear in the present tense if they would have been in the present tense when spoken. For example, at the end of Section 2, Hreidmar **took** the otter skin (*tók*, past tense) and **said** to the Æsir (*mælti*, past tense) that they **shall** fill and cover it with gold (*skulu*, present tense), and this **shall** be the terms (*skal*, present tense) of their settlement. This sentence is equivalent to: Hreidmar **took** the otter skin and **said** to the Æsir, "You **shall** fill and cover it with gold, and this **shall** be the terms of our settlement."

Af otrgjǫldum
Ór *Snorra Eddu, Skáldskaparmál* (46. kap.)

(About Otter's Ransom
From *The Prose Edda, Skáldskaparmál*
[*Poetic Diction* Section], Ch. 46)

1.

Hver sǫk er til þess,[48] at gull er kallat otrgjǫld?

Svá er sagt, at þá er Æsir fóru at kanna heim, Óðinn ok Loki ok Hœnir, þeir kómu at á nǫkkurri[49] ok gengu með ánni[50] til fors nǫkkurs, ok við forsinn var otr einn ok hann hafði tekit lax ór forsinum ok át blundandi.[51] Þá tók Loki upp stein ok kastaði at otrinum ok laust í hǫfuð honum.[52]

Þá hrósaði Loki veiði sinni, at hann hefði[53] veitt í einu hǫggvi otr ok lax; tóku þeir þá laxinn ok otrinn ok báru eptir sér,[54] kómu þá at bœ nǫkkurum ok gengu inn; en sá búandi er nefndr Hreiðmarr, er þar bjó, hann var mikill fyrir sér ok mjǫk fjǫlkunnigr; beiddusk Æsir at hafa þar

---

48 **Hver sǫk er til þess:** 'What is the reason' (*lit.* 'what reason is there for it').
49 **at á nǫkkurri:** 'to a certain river'.
50 **með ánni:** 'along the river [bank]'.
51 **át blundandi:** 'was eating [it] with eyes closed'.
52 **í hǫfuð honum:** 'into his head'.
53 **hefði:** 3sg. past subjunct. of *hafa*.
54 **báru eptir sér:** 'they carried [the otter and salmon] with them'.

náttstað ok kváðusk hafa með sér vist œrna[55] ok sýndu búandanum veiði sína.

Translate: ____

____

____

____

____

____

____

____

____

____

____

____

____

____

____

____

____

____

VOCABULARY

af *prep* [*w dat*] in regard to, concerning
at *prep* [*w dat*] at; to
at *inf marker* to
at *conj* that
á *f* river
ánni = **á** + **inni**
áss (*pl* æsir) *m* god; **Æsir** *pl* one of the two major groups of gods
át *3sg past of* **eta**
báru *3pl past of* **bera**
beiða (-dd-) *vb* [*w gen*] ask; *refl* **beiðask** request for oneself
beiddusk *3pl past refl of* **beiða**
bera (berr; bar, báru; borinn) *vb* carry, bear
bjó *3sg past of* **búa**
blunda (-að) *vb* shut the eyes, doze
blundandi *pres part of* **blunda**
búa (býr; bjó, bjoggu; búinn) *vb* live (in a place), dwell
búandi *m* farmer
bœr (*dat* bœ) *m* farm, farmstead, farmhouse
Edda *f* Edda (*literary work*); **Snorra Edda** 'Snorri's Edda', *The Prose Edda* written by Snorri Sturluson
einn *adj* a certain; *num* one
en *conj* but; and (on the other hand)
eptir *prep* [*w dat*] after, along with
er *rel particle* who, which, that; *conj* when; **þá er** when
er *vb* (it) is, (there) is (*3sg pres of* **vera**)
eta (etr; át, átu; etinn) *vb* eat
fara (ferr; fór, fóru; farinn) *vb* go,

[55] **kváðusk hafa með sér vist œrna:** 'they said they had sufficient provisions with them'.

travel; fare
fjǫlkunnigr *adj* skilled in magic, 'much knowing'
fors *m* waterfall
fóru *3pl past of* **fara**
fyrir *prep* [*w dat*] for, by; **fyrir sér** of oneself
ganga (gengr; gekk, gengu; genginn) *vb* go, walk
gengu *3pl past of* **ganga**
gjald *n* (*usu in pl* gjǫld) tribute; payment; reward; compensation; wergild (blood money)
gull *n* gold
hafa (hef(i)r, -ð-) *vb* have; hold
hann (*acc* hann, *dat* honum, *gen* hans) *pron* he
hefði *3sg past subjunct of* **hafa**
heimr *m* the world
honum *dat of* **hann**
Hreiðmarr *m* Hreidmar (*mythological name*), father of Otr, Fafnir, and Regin
hrósa (-að-) *vb* [*w dat*] boast (of)
hverr (-j-) *int pron* who, what, which
Hœnir *m* Hœnir (*mythological name*), one of the Æsir
hǫfuð *n* head
hǫgg (-v-) *n* stroke, blow
inn *adv* in (*motion*)
inn (*f* in, *n* it) *art* the
í *prep* [*w acc*] in, into (*motion*); [*w dat*] in, at (*location*)
kalla (-að-) *vb* call, name
kanna (-að-) *vb* explore
kapítuli *m* chapter
kasta (-að-) *vb* throw, cast
koma (kemr; kom, kómu/kvámu; kominn) *vb* come
kómu *3pl past of* **koma**
kváðusk *3pl past refl of* **kveða**
kveða (kveðr; kvað, kváðu; kveðinn) *vb* say; *refl* **kveðask** say of oneself [*w inf*]
laust *3sg past of* **ljósta**
lax *m* salmon
ljósta (lýstr; laust, lustu; lostinn) *vb* strike, hit
Loki *m* Loki (*mythological name*), the trickster god, one of the Æsir
mál *n* speech, language
með *prep* [*w dat*] with (accompanying); along
mikill (*n* mikit) *adj* big, large, great; **mikill fyrir sér** strong, powerful, mighty
mjǫk *adv* very, much, greatly
nátt *var of* **nótt**
náttstaðr *m* night-quarters, lodging for the night
nefna (-d-) *vb* name, call
nótt *f* night
nǫkkurr *indef pron* some, a certain
ok *conj* and
otr *m* otter
otrgjǫld *n pl* otter's ransom, wergild (blood money) for a dead otter
Óðinn *m* Odin (*mythological name*), chief god of the Æsir
ór *prep* [*w dat*] out of, from
sagt *ppart* (*n*) *of* **segja**
sá (*n* þat) *dem pron* that (one)
segja (sagð-) *vb* say, tell
sér *dat of* **sik**
sik (*dat* sér, *gen* sín) *refl pron* him-/her-/it-/oneself, themselves
sinn *refl poss adj* his, her, its, their (own)
sinni *f dat sg of* **sinn**
sína *f acc sg of* **sinn**
skáld *n* poet, 'skald'
Skáldskaparmál *n pl* 'Poetic Diction', the second section of *The Prose Edda*
skáldskapr (*gen* -ar) *m* poetry, 'skaldship'
Snorri *m* Snorri (*personal name*); Snorri Sturluson, author of *The Prose Edda*
staðr *m* place; stead
steinn *m* stone
svá *adv* so, thus; such
sýna (-d-) *vb* show
sǫk *f* reason, cause; **sǫk til [e-s]** reason for [sth], cause of [sth]
taka (tekr; tók, tóku; tekinn) *vb* take, catch, seize
tekit *ppart* (*n*) *of* **taka**
til *prep* [*w gen*] to, until
tók *3sg past of* **taka**
tóku *3pl past of* **taka**
upp *adv* up (*motion*)
var *3sg past of* **vera**
veiða (-dd-) *vb* catch
veiðr (*acc/dat* veiði) *f* catch
veitt *ppart* (*n*) *of* **veiða**
vera (er; var, váru; verit) *vb* be

vist *f* food, provisions
við *prep* [*w acc*] at, by, close to
þar *adv* there
þat (*gen* þess) *dem pron* that (one) (*n of* **sá**)
þá *adv* then; **þá er** *conj* when
þeir *pron* they (*m*)
þess *gen sg of* **þat**
Æsir *pl of* **Áss**
œrinn *adj* sufficient, enough

2.

En er Hreiðmarr sá otrinn, þá kallaði hann sonu sína, Fáfni ok Regin, ok segir, at Otr, bróðir þeira, var drepinn[56] ok svá, hverir þat hǫfðu gørt. Nú ganga þeir feðgar at Ásunum ok taka þá hǫndum ok binda ok segja þá um otrinn, at hann var sonr Hreiðmars.

Æsir bjóða fyrir sik fjǫrlausn,[57] svá mikit fé, sem Hreiðmarr sjálfr vill á kveða, ok varð þat at sætt með þeim[58] ok bundit svardǫgum.[59]

Þá var otrinn fleginn; tók Hreiðmarr otrbelginn ok mælti við þá, at þeir skulu fylla belginn af rauðu gulli ok svá hylja hann allan, ok skal þat vera at sætt þeira.

Translate: ____

____
____
____
____
____
____
____
____
____
____
____
____
____
____

VOCABULARY

af *prep* [*w dat*] of, with
allan *m acc sg* of **allr**
allr *adj/pron* all, entire, whole
at *prep* [*w dat*] for, as; **vera/verða at**

---

[56] **segir, at Otr, bróðir þeira, var drepinn:** an example of indirect speech with the verb in the indicative.
[57] **bjóða fyrir sik fjǫrlausn:** 'offered a ransom for their lives'.
[58] **varð þat at sætt með þeim:** 'that became the terms of the agreement (*lit.* that became as a settlement) between them'.
[59] **[varð] bundit svardǫgum:** '[it was] bound (or contracted) with oaths'.

sætt constitute a settlement or agreement
á *prep* [*w acc*] on (*motion*); [*w dat*] on (*location*); **kveða á** fix, determine
belgr *m* pelt, skin of an animal (taken off whole) ; skin-bag
binda (bindr; batt, bundu; bundinn) *vb* bind, tie, tie up
bjóða (býðr; bauð, buðu; boðinn) *vb* offer
bróðir *m* brother
bundit *ppart* (*n*) *of* **binda**
drepa (drepr; drap, drápu; drepinn) *vb* kill
Fáfnir *m* Fafnir (*personal name*); son of Hreidmar who turns himself into a dragon
feðgar *m pl* father and son(s)
fé *n* wealth, money
fjǫr (-v-) *n* life
fjǫrlausn *f* ransom for one's life
flá (flær; fló, flógu; fleginn) *vb* flay, strip
fleginn *ppart* (*m*) *of* **flá**
fylla (-d-) *vb* fill
fyrir *prep* [*w acc*] for, because of; **fyrir sik** for oneself, on one's own behalf
ganga (gengr; gekk, gengu; genginn) *vb* go, walk; **ganga at [e-m]** attack [sb]
gera (-ð-) *vb* do, make
gørt *var of* **gert**, *ppart* (*n*) *of* **gera**
hafa (hef(i)r, -ð-) *vb* have
hylja (hulð-) *vb* hide, cover
hǫfðu *3pl past of* **hafa**
hǫnd *f* hand; **taka hǫndum** take hold of, seize with the hands
kveða (kveðr; kvað, kváðu; kveðinn) *vb* say; **kveða á** fix, determine
lausn *f* ransom
með *prep* [*w dat*] with, between
mæla (-t-) *vb* say, speak; **mæla við** say to, speak to
nú *adv* now
Otr *m* Otr (*mythological name*), Otter, son of Hreidmar
otrbelgr *m* otter skin
rauðr *adj* red
Reginn *m* Regin (*mythological name*), son of Hreidmar and foster-father of Sigurd
sá *3sg past of* **sjá**
sem *conj* as
sína *m acc pl of* **sinn**
sjá (sér; sá, sá; sénn) *vb* see
sjálfr *adj* himself
skal *3 sg pres of* **skulu**
skulu (skal, skulu; skyldi; *pret inf* skyldu) *vb* shall (necessity), must
sonr (*pl acc* sonu) *m* son
svardagi *m* oath
svá *adv* so; **ok svá** and also
sætt *f* settlement, agreement, reconciliation; **vera/verða at sætt** constitute a settlement or agreement
taka (tekr; tók, tóku; tekinn) *vb* take, catch, seize; **taka hǫndum** take hold of, seize with the hands
um *prep* [*w acc*] about, in regard to
varð *3sg past of* **verða**
vera (er; var, váru; verit) *vb* be
verða (verðr; varð, urðu; orðinn) *vb* become
við *prep* [*w acc*] with; **mæla við** say to, speak to
vilja (vill; vildi; viljat; *pret inf* vildu) *vb* want, wish, will
þá *pron* them (*acc of* **þeir**)
þeim *pron* (to) them (*dat of* **þeir**)
þeir (*acc* þá, *dat* þeim, *gen* þeira) *pron* they (*m*)
þeir *dem pron* those (ones) (*m nom pl of* **sá**)
þeira *poss pron* their

3.

Þá sendi Óðinn Loka í Svartálfaheim, ok kom hann til dvergs þess, er heitir Andvari; hann var fiskr í vatni ok tók Loki hann hǫndum ok lagði á hann fjǫrlausn allt þat gull, er hann átti í steini sínum; ok er þeir koma í steininn, þá bar dvergrinn fram allt gull, þat er hann átti, ok var þat allmikit fé.

Þá svipti dvergrinn undir hǫnd sér einum litlum gullbaug; þat sá Loki ok bað hann fram láta bauginn. Dvergrinn bað hann eigi bauginn af sér taka[60] ok lézk mega œxla sér fé af bauginum, ef hann heldi.[61]

Translate: ____

____

____

____

____

____

____

____

____

____

____

____

____

Vocabulary

af *prep* [*w dat*] out of, from
allmikill *adj* very great
Andvari *m* Andvari (*personal name*), 'Vigilance', dwarf whose gold is used to pay Otr's wergild
álfr *m* elf
átti *3sg past of* **eiga**
bað *3sg past of* **biðja**
bar *3sg past of* **bera**
baugr (*dat* baug(i)) *m* ring
bera (berr; bar, báru; borinn) *vb* carry, bear
biðja (biðr; bað, báðu; beðinn) *vb* ask, request, bid
dvergr *m* dwarf
ef *conj* if
eiga (á, eigu; átti; áttr) *vb* own, possess
eigi *adv* not
fiskr *m* fish
fram *adv* forth
gullbaugr (*dat* gullbaug(i)) *m* gold ring
halda (heldr; helt, heldu; haldinn) *vb* hold; keep, retain
heita (heitir; hét, hétu; heitinn) *vb* be named, be called
heldi *3sg past subjunct of* **halda**
kom *3sg past of* **koma**
koma (kemr; kom, kómu/kvámu; kominn) *vb* come
lagði *3sg past of* **leggja**
láta (lætr; lét, létu; látinn) *vb* put, place, set; **láta fram** let go, yield, hand over; *refl* **látask** declare (of oneself)
leggja (lagð-) *vb* lay, place; set, fix, arrange; **leggja [e-t] á [e-n]** impose, lay [sth] upon [sb]
lézk *3sg past refl of* **láta**
litlum *m dat sg of* **lítill**
lítill (*dat m* litlum) *adj* little, small
mega (má, megu; mátti; mátt) *vb* be able
sá (*gen* þess) *dem pron* that (one)
senda (-nd-) *vb* send
sinn *refl poss adj* his, her, its, their

[60] **eigi bauginn af sér taka:** 'not to take the ring from him'.
[61] **lézk mega œxla sér fé af bauginum, ef hann heldi:** 'declared that he would be able to make more wealth for himself with the ring if he kept [it]'; *heldi*, 3sg. past subjunct. of *halda*.

(own)
sínum *m dat sg of* **sinn**
steinn *m* stone; stone dwelling, cave
Svartálfar *m pl* black elves
Svartálfheimr *m* world of the black elves
svartr *adj* black
svipta (-pt-) *vb* [*w dat*] sweep, pull quickly
undir *prep* [*w acc/dat*] under
vatn *n* water
þess *gen sg of* **sá**
œxla (-t-) *vb* multiply, increase

4.

Loki kvað hann eigi skyldu hafa einn penning eptir[62] ok tók bauginn af honum ok gekk út, en dvergrinn mælti, at sá baugr skyldi vera hverjum hǫfuðsbani, er ætti.[63]

Loki segir, at honum þótti þat vel, ok sagði, at þat skyldi haldask mega[64] fyrir því, sá formáli, at hann skyldi flytja þeim til eyrna, er þá tœki við.[65]

Fór hann í braut ok kom til Hreiðmars ok sýndi Óðni gullit; en er hann sá bauginn, þá sýndisk honum fagr ok tók hann af fénu, en greiddi Hreiðmari gullit.

Translate: __________

[62] **hann eigi skyldu hafa einn penning eptir:** 'he [the dwarf] should not have a coin left'; *skyldu*, pret. inf. of *skulu*.
[63] **sá baugr skyldi vera hverjum hǫfuðsbani, er ætti:** 'that ring would be death to everyone who possessed [it]'; *skyldi*, 3sg. past subjunct. of *skulu*; *ætti*, 3sg. past subjunct. of *eiga*.
[64] **þat skyldi haldask mega = þat skyldi mega haldask:** 'it would be able to hold true'.
[65] **er þá tœki við:** 'who would then receive [it]'; *tœki*, 3pl. past subjunct. of *taka*.

Vocabulary

braut *adv* away; **í braut** away
eiga (á, eigu; átti; áttr) *vb* own, possess
eptir *adv* behind, left over
eyra *n* ear
fagr *adj* beautiful, fair, fine
fénu = **fé** + **inu**
flytja (flutt-) *vb* convey, carry; deliver (an address), recite; **flytja til eyrna [e-m]** convey to the ears of [sb], inform [sb]
formáli *m* 'fore-speech', foretelling
fara (ferr; fór, fóru; farinn) *vb* go, travel; fare
fór *3sg past of* **fara**
fyrir *prep* [*w dat*] because of, for; **fyrir því, at** because
ganga (gengr; gekk, gengu; genginn) *vb* go, walk
gekk *3sg past of* **ganga**
greiða (-dd-) *vb* pay
halda (heldr; helt, heldu; haldinn) *vb* hold; keep, retain; *refl* **haldask** hold true, remain valid, stand
hverr (-j-) *indef pron* each, every(one)
hǫfuðsbani *m* death, destruction
kvað *3sg past of* **kveða**
kveða (kveðr; kvað, kváðu; kveðinn) *vb* say
penningr *m* penny, coin
sagði *3sg past of* **segja**
segja (sagð-) *vb* say, tell
skulu (skal, skulu; skyldi; *pret inf* skyldu) *vb* shall (necessity), must
skyldi *3sg past subjunct of* **skulu**
skyldu *pret inf of* **skulu**
sýna (-d-) *vb* show; *refl* **sýnask** [*w dat*] appear, seem (*impers*)
sýndisk *3sg past refl of* **sýna**
taka (tekr; tók, tóku; tekinn) *vb* take; **taka af** take away, remove from; **taka við** receive
tœki *3pl past subjunct of* **taka**
út *adv* out (*motion*)
vel *adv* well
þat (*dat* því) *dem pron* that (one)
þótti *3sg past of* **þykkja**
því *dat of* **þat**; **fyrir því, at** because
þykkja (þótt-) *vb* [*w dat*] seem (*impers*)
ætti *3sg past subjunct of* **eiga**

5.

Þá fylldi hann otrbelginn, sem mest mátti hann,[66] ok setti upp, er fullr var; gekk þá Óðinn til ok skyldi hylja belginn með gullinu,[67] ok þá mælti hann við Hreiðmar, at hann skal sjá, hvárt belgrinn er þá allr huldr; en Hreiðmarr leit á vandliga ok sá eitt granahár ok bað þat hylja, en at ǫðrum kosti væri lokit sætt þeira.[68] Þá dró Óðinn fram bauginn, ok hulði granahárit ok sagði, at þá váru þeir lausir frá otrgjǫldunum.

En er Óðinn hafði tekit geir sinn, en Loki skúa sína, ok þurftu þá ekki at óttask,[69] þá mælti Loki, at þat skyldi haldask, er Andvari hafði mælt, at sá baugr ok þat gull skyldi verða þess bani, er ætti, ok þat helzk síðan.

Nú er sagt, af hverju gull er otrgjǫld kallat eða nauðgjald Ásanna eða rógmálmr.

---

[66] **sem mest mátti hann:** 'as much as he was able'.
[67] **skyldi hylja belginn með gullinu:** 'he went to cover the skin with the gold'.
[68] **en at ǫðrum kosti væri lokit sætt þeira:** 'or otherwise their agreement would be ended'.
[69] **en [er] Loki [hafði tekit] skúa sína, ok þurftu þá ekki at óttask:** 'and [when] Loki [had taken] his shoes, and they then had no need to fear'.

Translate: ____

____

____

____

____

____

____

____

____

____

____

____

____

____

____

____

____

VOCABULARY

annarr (*dat m* ǫðrum) *adj* other, another; **at ǫðrum kosti** otherwise
bani *m* death
draga (dregr; dró, drógu; dreginn) *vb* draw, pull
dró *3sg past of* **draga**
eða *conj* or
einn (*n* eitt) *num* one
eitt *n of* **einn**
ekki *indef pron* (*n*), nothing (*see* **engi**); *as adv* not
engi *indef pron* no one; (*n* **ekki**) nothing
frá *prep* [*w dat*] from
fullr *adj* full
ganga (gengr; gekk, gengu; genginn) *vb* go, walk; **ganga til** approach, go up to a thing
geirr *m* spear
granahár *n* whisker
grǫn (*pl gen* grana) *f* lip
halda (heldr; helt, heldu; haldinn) *vb* hold; keep, retain; *refl* **haldask** hold true, remain valid, stand
hár *n* hair
helzk *3sg past refl of* **halda**
hulði *3sg past of* **hylja**
huldr *ppart* (*m*) *of* **hylja**
hvárt *conj* whether
hverr (-j-) *int pron* who; (*n*) what; **af hverju** why, for what reason
hylja (huld/hulð-) *vb* hide, cover
kostr *m* choice, alternative; **at ǫðrum kosti** otherwise
lauss *adj* free
líta (lítr; leit, litu; litinn) *vb* look; **líta á** look at, consider
lokit *ppart* (*n*) *of* **lúka**
lúka (lýkr; lauk, luku; lokinn) *vb* [*w dat*] end, finish
málmr *m* ore; metal
mátti *3sg past of* **mega**
með prep [*w dat*] with, by, using
mega (má, megu; mátti; mátt) *vb* be able
mest *superl adv* most (*see* **mjǫk**); **sem mest** as much as possible
mjǫk (*superl* mest) *adv* much
nauð *f* need
nauðgjald *n* forced payment
óttask (-að-) *refl vb* fear
róg *f* stife, discord

rógmálmr *m* metal of strife
sem *conj* as; **sem mest** as much as possible
setja (-tt-) *vb* set, put, place
síðan *adv* then, later, afterwards, after that
skór (*pl* skúar) *m* shoe
skulu (skal, skulu; skyldi; *pret inf* skyldu) *vb* shall (necessity), must
skúa *acc pl of* **skór**
skyldi *3sg past, 3sg and 3pl past subjunct of* **skulu**
vandliga *adv* carefully
váru *3pl past of* **vera**
vera (er; var, váru; verit) *vb* be
væri *3sg past subjunct of* **vera**
þurfa (þarf, þurfu; þurfti; þurft) *vb* need

Frá Fáfni, Regin ok Sigurði
Ór *Snorra Eddu, Skáldskaparmál* (47. kap.)
(About Fafnir, Regin, and Sigurd
From *The Prose Edda, Skáldskaparmál*, Ch. 47)

1.

Hvat er fleira at segja frá gullinu?

Hreiðmarr tók þá gullit at sonargjǫldum,[70] en Fáfnir ok Reginn beiddusk af nǫkkurs í bróðurgjǫld.[71] Hreiðmarr unni þeim enskis pennings af gullinu. Þat varð óráð þeira brœðra, at þeir drápu fǫður sinn til gullsins.

Þá beiddisk Reginn, at Fáfnir skyldi skipta gullinu í helminga með þeim.[72] Fáfnir svarar svá, at lítil ván var,[73] at hann myndi miðla gullit við bróður sinn, er hann drap fǫður sinn til gullsins, ok bað Regin fara braut, en at ǫðrum kosti myndi hann fara sem Hreiðmarr.[74]

Translate: ____

____

____

____

____

____

____

____

[70] **at sonargjǫldum:** 'as ransom for [his] son'.
[71] **beiddusk af nǫkkurs í bróðurgjǫld:** 'requested some of it for themselves in ransom for [their] brother'.
[72] **með þeim:** 'between them'.
[73] **lítil ván var:** 'there was little likelihood'.
[74] **myndi hann fara sem Hreiðmarr:** 'he would fare [the same] as Hreidmar' (i.e., he would share the same fate as Hreidmar).

Vocabulary

bróðir (*acc/dat/gen* bróður; *pl gen* brœðra) *m* brother
bróðurgjǫld *n pl* ransom, wergild (blood money) for a brother
brœðra *gen pl of* **bróðir**
drap *3sg past of* **drepa**
drápu *3pl past of* **drepa**
drepa (drepr; drap, drápu; drepinn) *vb* kill
engi (*gen m/n* enskis) *indef pron* no one, not one
enskis *m/n gen sg of* **engi**
faðir (*acc/dat/gen* fǫður) *m* father
fleiri *comp adj* more (*see* **margr**)
fleira *n of* **fleiri**
frá *prep* [*w dat*] about; **segja frá** tell about
fǫður *acc sg of* **faðir**
helmingr *m* half; **skipta í helminga** divide into two equal portions
hvat *int pron* what (*n of* **hverr**)
hverr (*n* hvat) *int pron* who; what, which
margr (*comp* fleiri) *adj* [*w sg*] many a (in collective sense); [*w pl*] many
miðla (-að-) *vb* share
munu (mun, munu; mundi; *pret inf* mundu) *vb* will, shall (*future*)
myndi *3sg past subjunct of* **munu**
óráð *n* evil plan, ill-advised plan
sá (*pl* þeir) *dem pron* that (one)
Sigurðr *m* Sigurd (*personal name*); legendary hero who slays Fafnir the dragon
skipta (-pt-) *vb* [*w dat*] divide, share; **skipta í helminga** divide into two equal portions
sonargjǫld *n pl* ransom, wergild (blood money) for a son
svara (-að-) *vb* answer, reply
til *prep* [*w gen*] to; for; with respect to, for the sake of
unna (ann, unnu; unni; unn(a)t) *vb* [*w dat of person, gen of thing*] grant, allow
ván *f* expectation, prospect
þeir (*gen* þeira) *dem pron/adj* those (*m nom pl of* **sá**)
þeira *dem adj* of those (*gen of* **þeir**)

2.

Fáfnir hafði þá tekit hjálm, er Hreiðmarr hafði átt, ok setti á hǫfuð sér,[75] er kallaðr var Œgishjálmr, [sá] er ǫll kvikvendi hræðask, er sjá,[76] ok sverð þat, er Hrotti heitir.

Reginn hafði þat sverð, er Refill er kallaðr; flýði hann þá braut, en Fáfnir fór upp á Gnitaheiði ok gerði sér þar ból ok brásk í ormslíki ok

[75] **setti á hǫfuð sér:** 'he set [it] on his head'.
[76] **er kallaðr var Œgishjálmr, [sá] er ǫll kvikvendi hræðask, er sjá:** 'which was called Helmet-of-Terror, [that one] which all living things fear who see [it]'.

lagðisk á gullit,[77] en Reginn fór þá til Hjálpreks konungs á Þjóði[78] ok gerðisk þar smiðr hans. Þá tók hann þar til fóstrs Sigurð,[79] son Sigmundar, sonar Vǫlsungs, ok son Hjǫrdísar, dóttur Eylima.

Translate: ____

____

____

____

____

____

____

____

____

____

____

____

____

____

Vocabulary

allr (*pl n* ǫll) *adj/pron* all
átt *ppart* (*n*) *of* **eiga**
ból *n* lair
brásk *3sg past refl of* **bregða**
bregða (bregðr; brá, brugðu; brugðinn) *vb* [*w dat*] alter, change; *refl* **bregðask** change oneself into another shape
dóttir (*acc/dat/gen* dóttur) *f* daughter
eiga (á, eigu; átti; áttr) *vb* own, possess
Eylimi *m* Eylimi (*personal name*); legendary king, father of Hjordis
flýja (-ð-) to flee
fóstr (*gen* -rs) *n* fostering, fosterage
gera (-ð-) *vb* do, make; *refl* **gerask** become
gerðisk *3sg past refl of* **gera**
Gnitaheiðr (*gen* -ar) *f* Gnitaheath (*place name*), where Fafnir, as a dragon, lies upon great wealth
hans *poss pron* his
heiðr *f* heath
hjálmr *m* helmet
Hjálprekr *m* Hjalprek (*personal name*), a legendary king
Hjǫrdís *f* Hjordis (*personal name*); mother of Sigurd
Hrotti *m* Hrotti (*mythological name*), name of a sword
hræða (-dd-) *vb* [*w acc*] frighten; *refl* **hræðask** be frightened; **hræðask [e-t]** be afraid of [sth]
konungr *m* king
kvikvendi *n pl* living creatures, animals, beasts
lagðisk *3sg past refl of* **leggja**
leggja (lagð-) *vb* lay, place; *refl* **leggjask** lay oneself, lie down
líki *n* form, shape, likeness
ormr *m* snake, serpent
ormslíki *n* form of a snake

---

[77] **lagðisk á gullit:** 'laid himself upon the gold'.
[78] **á Þjóði:** the modern province of Thy in northern Jutland, Denmark.
[79] **þá tók hann þar til fóstrs Sigurð:** 'then he took Sigurd there [at that place] in fosterage'.

Refill *m* Refil (*mythological name*), name of a sword
Sigmundr (*gen* -ar) *m* Sigmund (*personal name*); son of Volsung and father of Sigurd
smiðr *m* smith
sonr (*gen* -ar) *m* son
sverð *n* sword
Vǫlsungr *m* Volsung (*personal name*); father of Sigmund
Þjóð *f* Thjod 'People' (*place name*, modern province of Thy in Jutland, Denmark)
œgir (*gen* -is) *m* one who frightens
œgishjálmr *m* helmet of dread
ǫll *n pl of* **allr**

3.

Sigurðr var ágætastr allra herkonunga af ætt ok afli ok hug. Reginn sagði honum til, hvar Fáfnir lá[80] á gullinu, ok eggjaði hann at sœkja gullit.

Þá gerði Reginn sverð þat, er Gramr heitir, er svá var hvast, at Sigurðr brá niðr í rennanda vatn, ok tók í sundr ullarlagð, er rak fyrir strauminum at sverðsegginni.[81] Því næst klauf Sigurðr steðja Regins ofan í stokkinn með sverðinu.[82]

Translate: ____

____

____

____

____

____

____

____

____

____

Vocabulary

af *prep* [*w dat*] on account of, by reason of
afl *n* strength
ágætr (*superl* ágætastr) *adj* excellent, outstanding
brá *3sg past of* **bregða**
bregða (bregðr; brá, brugðu; brugðinn) *vb* [*w dat*] thrust
egg (-j-) *f* edge
eggja (-að-) *vb* egg on, urge, incite
fyrir *prep* [*w dat*] before, with; **fyrir strauminum** with the current
Gramr *m* Gram (*mythological name*), name of Sigurd the Dragon Slayer's sword
herkonungr *m* warrior-king
herr *m* army
hugr (*dat* hug) *m* courage
hvar *int adv* where
hvass *adj* sharp

80 **sagði honum til, hvar Fáfnir lá:** 'informed him of where Fafnir lay'.
81 **er svá var hvast, at ... at sverðsegginni:** 'which was so sharp that Sigurd thrust [it] down into running water and cut apart a tuft of wool that drifted with the current against the sword's edge'.
82 **ofan í stokkinn:** 'down to the stock' (on which the anvil was sitting).

klauf *3sg past of* **kljúfa**
kljúfa (klýfr; klauf, klufu; klofinn) *vb* split, cleave
lagðr *m* tuft (of wool or hair)
lá *3sg past of* **liggja**
liggja (liggr; lá, lágu; leginn) *vb* lie
næst *adv* next (following); **því næst** then, next, thereupon
ofan *adv* down, from above
rak *3sg past of* **reka**
reka (rekr; rak, ráku; rekinn) *vb* be carried along, drift; **reka fyrir strauminum** drift with the current
renna (rennr; rann, runnu; runninn) *vb* run, flow
rennandi *pres part of* **renna**
segja (sagð-) *vb* say, tell; **segja til** tell, inform of
steði (-ja) *m* anvil
stokkr *m* stock of an anvil
straumr *m* stream, current
sundr (*also* **í sundr**) *adv* apart, asunder
svá *adv* so; **svá ... at** so ... that
sverðsegg (-j-) *f* sword's edge
sœkja (sótt-) *vb* seek
taka (tekr; tók, tóku; tekinn) *vb* take; **taka í sundr** cut in two
ull *f* wool
ullarlagðr *m* tuft of wool
ætt *f* family

4.

Eptir þat fóru þeir Sigurðr ok Reginn á Gnitaheiði; þá gróf Sigurðr grǫf á veg Fáfnis ok settisk þar í.[83] En er Fáfnir skreið til vatns ok hann kom yfir grǫfina, þá lagði Sigurðr sverðinu í gøgnum hann, ok var þat hans bani.

Kom þá Reginn at ok sagði, at hann hefði drepit bróður hans, ok bauð honum þat at sætt, at hann skyldi taka hjarta Fáfnis ok steikja við eld, en Reginn lagðisk niðr ok drakk blóð Fáfnis ok lagðisk at sofa.

En er Sigurðr steikði hjartat ok hann hugði, at fullsteikt myndi,[84] ok tók á fingrinum, hvé hart var;[85] en er frauðit rann ór hjartanu á fingrinn, þá brann hann ok drap fingrinum í munn sér; en er hjartablóðit kom á tunguna, þá kunni hann fuglsrǫdd ok skildi, hvat igðurnar sǫgðu, er sátu í viðnum.

Translate: ____

____

____

____

____

____

____

____

____

[83] **settisk þar í:** 'settled himself in it (*lit.* therein)'.
[84] **hugði, at fullsteikt myndi:** 'thought that it was [probably] fully roasted'.
[85] **tók á fingrinum, hvé hart var:** touched [it] with [his] finger [to see] how hard it was'.

Vocabulary

bauð *3sg past of* **bjóða**
bjóða (býðr; bauð, buðu; boðinn) *vb* [*w acc of person, dat of thing*] offer
blóð *n* blood
brann *3sg past of* **brenna**
brenna (brennr; brann, brunnu; brunninn) *vb* burn
drakk *3sg past of* **drekka**
drekka (drekkr; drakk, drukku; drukkinn) *vb* drink
drepa (drepr; drap, drápu; drepinn) *vb* kill; [*w dat*] put
eldr *m* fire
eptir *prep* [w acc] after (*time*)
fingr *m* finger
frauð *n* froth, juice (of roasted meat)
fugl *m* bird
fuglsrǫdd *f* bird's voice, speech of birds
fullsteiktr *ppart* fully roasted (*from* **steikja**)
grafa (grefr; gróf, grófu; grafinn) *vb* dig
gróf *3sg past of* **grafa**
grǫf *f* pit, ditch
harðr (*n* hart) *adj* hard
hjarta *n* heart
hjartablóð *n* heart's blood
hugði *3sg past of* **hyggja**
hvé *adv* how, to what extent
hyggja (hugð-) *vb* think
gegnum (*also* **í gegnum**) *prep* [*w acc*] through
gøgnum = **gegnum**
igða *f* nuthatch (species of bird)
igðurnar = **igður** + **innar**
koma (kemr; kom, kómu/kvámu; kominn) *vb* come; **koma at** arrive
kunna (kann, kunnu; kunni; kunnat) *vb* know, understand
leggja (lagð-) *vb* lay, place; **leggja [e-u] í gegnum [e-n]** thrust [sth] through [sb]; *refl* **leggjask** lay oneself, lie down; **leggjask at sofa** go to sleep
munnr *m* mouth
niðr *adv* down
rann *3sg past of* **renna**
renna (rennr; rann, runnu; runninn) *vb* run, flow
rǫdd *f* voice
sátu *3pl past of* **sitja**
segja (sagð-) *vb* say, tell
setja (-tt-) *vb* set, put, place; *refl* **setjask** settle oneself, sit down
settisk *3sg past refl of* **setja**
sitja (sitr; sat, sátu; setinn) *vb* sit
skilja (-d-) *vb* discern, understand
skreið *3sg past of* **skríða**
skríða (skríðr; skreið, skriðu; skriðinn) *vb* crawl, creep
sofa (sefr; svaf, sváfu; sofinn) *vb* sleep
steikja (-t/ð-) *vb* roast
sǫgðu *3pl past of* **segja**
taka (tekr; tók, tóku; tekinn) *vb* reach, stretch forth, touch; **taka á** touch
tunga *f* tongue
vegr *m* way, path
viðr (*dat* við(i)) *m* tree
yfir *prep* [*w acc/dat*] over, above

5.

Þá mælti ein:[86] ____________________

Þar sitr Sigurðr ____________________
sveita stokkinn, ____________________
Fáfnis hjarta ____________________
við funa steikir; ____________________
spakr þœtti mér ____________________
spillir bauga, ____________________
ef fjǫrsega ____________________
fránan æti. ____________________

Þar liggr Reginn – ____________________
kvað ǫnnur, ____________________
ræðr um við sik, ____________________
vill tæla mǫg, ____________________
þann es[87] trúir honum; ____________________
berr af reiði, ____________________
rǫng orð saman, ____________________
vill bǫlvasmiðr, ____________________
bróður hefna. ____________________

Vocabulary

annarr (*f* ǫnnur) *adj* other, another
bera (berr; bar, báru; borinn) *vb* carry, bear; **bera saman** collect, gather together
bǫl (-v-) *n* trouble, misfortune, 'bale'
bǫlvasmiðr *m* trouble-smith, forger of misfortune
es = **er**
eta (etr; át, átu; etinn) *vb* eat
fjǫrsegi *m* heart ('life-muscle')
fránn *adj* gleaming, flashing
funi *m* flame
hefna (-d-) *vb* avenge
mǫgr *m* boy, youth
orð *n* word
ráða (ræðr; réð, réðu; ráðinn) *vb* [*w dat*] advise, counsel; decide, determine; **ráða um við [e-n]** consult with [sb]
rangr (*pl n* rǫng) *adj* wrong; crooked
reiði *f* anger
ræðr *3sg pres of* **ráða**
saman *adv* together; **bera saman** collect, gather together
sá (*acc* þann) *dem pron* that (one)
segi *m* slice, strip, shred
spakr *adj* wise
spilla (-t-) *vb* [*w dat*] spoil, destroy
spillir *m* spoiler; **spillir bauga** *poet* generous lord, spoiler (= distributor) of rings
stokkinn *ppart* spattered, stained (*esp* with blood) (*from* **støkkva**)
støkkva (støkkr; stǫkk, stukku; stokkinn) *vb* be sprinkled, spattered
sveiti *m* blood

[86] **ein** = **ein [igða]:** 'one [nuthatch]'.
[87] **es** = **er**.

tæla (-d-) *vb* betray; entice, entrap
trúa (-ð-) *vb* [*w dat*] trust
þann *acc of* **sá**
þykkja (þótt-) *vb* [*w dat*] seem (*impers*)
þœtti *3sg past subjunct of* **þykkja**
æti *3sg past subjunct of* **eta**
ǫnnur *f of* **annarr**

6.

Þá gekk Sigurðr til Regins ok drap hann, en síðan til hests síns, er Grani heitir, ok reið, til þess er hann kom til bóls Fáfnis, tók þá upp gullit ok batt í klyfjar ok lagði upp á bak Grana ok steig upp sjálfr ok reið þá leið sína.

Nú er þat sagt, hver saga til er þess, at[88] gullit er kallat ból eða bygð Fáfnis eða málmr Gnitaheiðar eða byrðr Grana.

Translate: ______________________________

Vocabulary

bak *n* back
batt *3sg past of* **binda**
binda (bindr; batt, bundu; bundinn) *vb* bind, tie, tie up
bygð *f* home, settlement, abode
byrðr *f* burden, load
Grani *m* Grani (*mythological name*), Sigurd the Dragon-Slayer's horse
klyf (*pl* -jar) *f* pack (for a horse)
leið *f* way, road
málmr *m* metal
reið *3sg past of* **ríða**
ríða (ríðr; reið, riðu; riðinn) *vb* ride, go on horseback; **ríða leið sína** ride on his way
sinn *refl poss adj* his, her, its, their (own)
síns *m gen sg of* **sinn**
steig *3sg past of* **stíga**
stíga (stígr; steig/sté, stigu; stiginn) *vb* step (up); **stíga á bak** mount on horseback
til *prep* [*w gen*] to, until; **til þess** the reason for this; **til þess er** until

[88] **hver saga til er þess [= er til þess]:** 'the story of why' (*lit.* 'what story is [the reason] for it').

Vocabulary

Words are alphabetized employing the following conventions.

- *ð* is listed with *d*.
- *þ*, *æ*, *œ*, *ǫ*, *ø* come at the end of the alphabet in that order.
- Short vowels and long vowels are treated as separate letters. Words beginning with a short (unaccented) vowel are alphabetized ahead of words beginning with a long (accented) vowel. The same rule applies to short and long vowels within a word. For example, *austr* comes before *á*, and *farmaðr* comes before *fá*.

a, á, b, d, ð, e, é, f, g, h, i, í, j, k, l, m, n, o, ó,
p, r, s, t, u, ú, v, x, y, ý, z, þ, æ, œ, ǫ(ö), ø

Principal parts of verbs are listed as follows:

- Weak verbs:
  infinitive (dental suffix or past-tense stem)
- Strong verbs:
  infinitive (3sg. pres.; 3sg. past, 3pl. past; ppart.)
- Preterite-present verbs:
  infinitive (3sg. pres, 3pl. pres.; 3sg past; ppart or pret. inf.)

Where phrases and idioms are listed, the Icelandic convention of using the pronouns **einnhverr** 'somebody' [sb] and **eitthvat** 'something' [sth] has been adopted to indicate which case the object of a verb or preposition takes, and to distinguish whether the object is a person or thing.

[e-n] (**einhvern**) =somebody [sb] *acc*
[e-t] (**eitthvat**) =something [sth] *acc*
[e-m] (**einhverjum**) =(for) [sb] *dat*
[e-u] (**einhverju**) =(for) [sth] *dat*
[e-s] (**einhvers**) =(of) [sb] or [sth] *gen*

Examples:

fala [e-t] af [e-m] offer to buy [sth] from [sb]
firra [e-n] [e-u] deprive [sb] of [sth]
mæla [e-t] við [e-n] say [sth] to [sb]
segja [e-m] frá [e-m] tell, inform [sb] about [sb]
segja [e-m] til [e-s] tell, inform [sb] where [sth/sb] is to be found

A

Aðalból *n* Adalbol (*place name*)
Aðalsteinn *m* Athelstane (*personal name*)
Aðils *m* Adils (*personal name*)
aðrar *adj, see* **annarr**
af *prep* [*w dat*] off, out of, from; of; with; in regard to, concerning; on account of, by reason of; **skjóta af** shoot with
af *adv* off, away; **verða af** come about, appear
afarkostir *m pl* hard terms
afl *n* strength; **sterkr at afli** strong
aka (ekr; ók, óku; ekinn) *vb* drive
aldar, **aldir** *f, see* **ǫld**
aldr *m* age, life; **á ungum aldri** young, of a young age
aldri *adv* never
aldrlag *n* fate, destiny; end of life
Alfǫðr *m* 'All-Father', a name of Odin
allmikill *adj* very great
allr (*f* ǫll, *n* allt) *adj/pron* all, entire, whole; **um alla hluti** in all respects; **alls konar** of every kind, of all kinds; **allra helzt** especially, most of all; **at ǫllu** in all respects
allvaldr *m* sovereign, king
alskipaðr *adj* fully manned
alt *adv* all the way
alvara *f* earnestness, seriousness
alþýða *f* all the people, the majority of people, the public, the common people
Andvari *m* Andvari ('Vigilance') (*personal name*), dwarf whose gold is used to pay Otr's wergild
annarr (*f* ǫnnur, *n* annat; *acc m* annan, *f* aðra, *dat m* ǫðrum, *n* ǫðru; *pl m* aðrir, etc.) *adj* other, another; second; **annarr ... annarr ...** *indef pron* the one ... the other ...; **at ǫðrum kosti** otherwise
aptr *adv* back
arfr *m* inheritance
Arinbjǫrn *m* Arinbjorn (*personal name*)
armr (*f* ǫrm, *n* armt) *adj* wretched, vile, wicked; poor, unfortunate
Arnarstakkr *m* 'Eagle's Haystack', a mountain in the south of Iceland (*place name*)
Arnarstakksheiðr *f* Heath of Arnarstakkr (*place name*)
askr *m* ash (tree)
at *prep* [*w dat*] at, to; with respect to; for, as; **auðigr at fé** wealthy; **kærr at** fond of; **sterkr at afli** strong; **vera/verða at sætt** constitute a settlement or agreement
at *adv* **berask at** happen; **[e-t] er/var at** it is/was [sth]; **gaman sé at** it is amusing
at *conj* that; so that
at *inf marker* to
auðigr *adj* wealthy; **auðigr at fé** wealthy
Auðhumla *f* Audhumla (*mythological name*, the primeval cow)
Auðr *f* Aud (*personal name*)
auga *n* eye
auka (eykr; jók, jóku; aukinn) *vb* increase
Aurland *n* Aurland (*place name*)
ausa (eyss; jós, jósu/jusu; ausinn) *vb* sprinkle, pour
austr *adv* east
austanverðr *adj* eastern

Á

á *prep* [*w acc*] on, onto, into (*motion*); with respect to; [*w dat*] on, at, in (*location*); **á dǫgum** in the days; **á einu hverju sumri** one summer; **á himni** in heaven; **á lífi** alive; **á ungum aldri** young; **fegrð á hár (líki)** beauty of hair (body); **kveða á** fix, determine
á *adv* **á brott** away; **hversu lízk þér á** how do you like
á (*gen* ár; *pl* ár, *dat* ám, *gen* á) *f* river
á *vb, see* **eiga**
áðr *adv* before, already; *conj* before
ágætr (*superl* ágætastr) *adj* excellent, outstanding
Álfheimr *m* 'Land of the Elves' (*place

name)
álfr *m* elf
Álfr *m* Alf ('Elf') (*personal name*)
álit *n* appearance, countenance; **fagr álitum** beautiful (in appearance), handsome
ár *n* year
Ásgerðr *f* Asgerd (*personal name*)
áss (*dat* æsi/ás, *gen* áss/ásar; *pl* æsir, *acc* ásu/æsi) *m* god; **Æsir** *pl* one of the two major groups of gods
át *vb, see* **eta**
átján *num* eighteen
átt, átti, áttar *vb, see* **eiga**
átta *num* eight

B

bað *vb, see* **biðja**
bak *n* back
Baldr *m* Baldr (*mythological name*)
bani *m* death
banna (-að-) *vb* forbid, prohibit; **banna jarðir at byggja ok vinna** forbid lands to be rented and worked
bar *vb, see* **bera**
bardagi *m* battle
barðisk *vb, see* **berja**
barn (*pl* bǫrn) *n* child
barsk, báru *vb, see* **bera**
batt *vb, see* **binda**
bauð *vb, see* **bjóða**
baugr (*dat* baug(i)) *m* ring
bazk *vb, see* **biðja**
báðir (*f* báðar, *n* bæði, *gen* beggja) *adj/pron dual* both
báru *vb, see* **bera**
beðit *vb, see* **biðja**
beiða (-dd-) *vb* [*w gen*] ask; *refl* **beiðask** request for oneself
bein *n* bone
beinlauss *adj* boneless
bekkr (*dat* bekk, *gen* -jar; *pl* -ir) *m* bench
belgr (*dat* belg, *gen* -s/jar; *pl* -ir) *m* pelt, skin of an animal (taken off whole); skin-bag; bellows
bera (berr; bar, báru; borinn) *vb* carry, bear; **bera saman** collect, gather together; **bera út á** carry out into; **bera vápn á [e-n]** raise weapons against [sb]; **vel viti borinn** intelligent, endowed with good sense; *refl* **berask at** happen
berg *n* rock, boulder
berja (barð-) *vb* beat, strike, smite; *refl* **berjask** fight
betr *comp adv* better (*see* **vel**)
betri *comp adj* better (*see* **góðr**)
bezt *superl adv* best (*see* **vel**)
beztr *superl adj* best (*see* **góðr**)
biðja (biðr; bað, báðu; beðinn) *vb* ask, request, bid; [*w gen*] ask for, request; **biðja konu** ask for a woman in marriage; *refl* **biðjask undan** be evasive
Bifrǫst *f* the rainbow bridge to heaven
bik *n* pitch
bil *n* moment
binda (bindr; batt, bundu; bundinn) *vb* bind, tie, tie up
bitu *vb, see* **bíta**
bíta (bítr; beit, bitu; bitinn) *vb* bite
Bjarnardóttir *f* daughter of Bjorn
bjartr *adj* bright, radiant
bjó *vb, see* **búa**
bjóða (býðr; bauð, buðu; boðinn) *vb* [*w acc of person, dat of thing*] offer
bjósk *vb, see* **búa**
Bjǫrgyn (*dat* Bjǫrgyn) *m* Bergen, Norway (*place name*)
bjǫrn (*dat* birni, *gen* bjarnar; *pl* birnir, *acc* bjǫrnu) *m* bear
Bjǫrn (*dat* Birni, *gen* Bjarnar) *m* Bjorn ('Bear') (*personal name*)
blása (blæss; blés, blésu; blásinn) *vb* blow
blóð *n* blood
blót *n* sacrifice
blunda (-að) *vb* shut the eyes, doze
boð *n* bidding, command; message
bogi *m* bow; **kom á boga Einars miðjan** struck the middle of Einars bow
bogmaðr *m* archer
borg (*pl* -ir) *f* stronghold, fortification; town
Borg *f* Borg (*place name*)
Borgarfjǫrðr *m* 'Borg's Fjord', a fjord in Western Iceland (*place name*)
borinn *ppart, see* **bera**

botn (*gen* botns; *pl* botnar) *m* bottom; head of a bay, lake, dale, etc.
bók (*pl* bœkr) *f* book
ból *n* lair
bóndi (*pl* bœndr) *see* **búandi**
bónorð *n* request, petition; **hefja upp bónorð** propose marriage
bragð *n* sudden, brisk movement; moment; **af bragði**, soon
brann *vb*, *see* **brenna**
brast *vb*, *see* **bresta**
braut *var of* **brot(t)**
brá *f* eyelash
brá, **brásk** *vb*, *see* **bregða**
brátt *adv* quickly
Brávǫllr *m* Brávoll, a plain in Sweden (*place name*)
bregða (bregðr; brá, brugðu; brugðinn) *vb* [*w dat*] cause to move; thrust (a weapon); alter, change; *refl* **bregðask** change oneself into another shape
Breiðablik *n* Breidablik ('Broad Gleam') (*mythological place name*)
brenna (brennr; brann, brunnu; brunninn) *vb* burn
bresta (brestr; brast, brustu; brostinn) *vb* break
brestr (*pl* -ir) *m* break, crash; **eigi mun svá mikill brestr orðinn** such a great break is not likely to have occurred
brjósk *n* cartilage
brjóta (brýtr; braut, brutu; brotinn) *vb* break
brot(t) *adv* **á brott** away (*motion*); **í brot(t)** away (*motion*)
brottu *adv* **í brottu** away (*location*)
bróðir (*acc/dat/gen* bróður; *pl* brœðr, *dat* brœðr, *gen* brœðra) *m* brother
bróðurgjǫld *n pl* ransom, wergild (blood money) for a brother
brók (*pl* brœkr) *f* pants-leg; breeches
brunnr *m* well
brúarsporðr *m* bridge-head
brúðlaup *n* wedding; **gera brúðlaup til** marry
brynja *f* coat of mail
Brynjólfr *m* Brynjolf (*personal name*)
brýtr *vb*, *see* **brjóta**
brœðr, **brœðra** *m pl*, *see* **bróðir**
bundit *ppart*, *see* **binda**
Buri *m* Buri (*personal name*)
búa (býr; bjó, bjoggu; búinn) *vb* live (in a place), dwell; *refl* **búask** prepare (oneself); **búask til** prepare (oneself) for; **undir at búa** to bear up under
búandi (*also* **bóndi**) (*pl* búendr) *m* farmer; head of a household
búð (*pl* -ir) *f* tent, booth
bygð *f* home, settlement, abode
byggja (bygð-) *vb* inhabit, dwell; rent, let out
byrðr *f* burden, load
byrr (*gen* -jar; *pl* -ir) *m* fair wind; **[e-m] gefr vel byri** *impers* [sb] gets fair winds
býr, **býsk** *vb*, *see* **búa**
bǫrn *n pl*, *see* **barn**
bæði *adv* both
bœkr *f pl*, *see* **bók**
bœndr *m pl*, *see* **bóndi**
bœr (*dat* bœ, *gen* bœjar; *pl* bœir) *m* farm, farmstead; farmhouse
bœta (-tt-) *vb* better, improve
bǫl (-v-) *n* trouble, misfortune, 'bale'
bǫlvasmiðr *m* trouble-smith, forger of misfortune

D

dagr *m* day; **á dǫgum** in the days (of); **í dag** today; **þann dag** on that day
dalr (*dat* dal(i)) *m* valley, dale
Danmǫrk (*dat* Danmǫrku) *f* Denmark
dauðr (*n* dautt) *adj* dead
deyja (deyr; dó, dóu; dáinn) *vb* die
deila *f* dispute
djúpr *adj* deep
dóttir (*acc/dat/gen* dóttur; *pl* dœtr, *dat* dœtrum, *gen* dœtra) *f* daughter
draga (dregr; dró, drógu; dreginn) *vb* pull, draw; **draga fyrir** draw beyond; **draga saman** assemble
drakk *vb*, *see* **drekka**
drap *vb*, *see* **drepa**
draup *vb*, *see* **drjúpa**
drápu *vb*, *see* **drepa**
dregr *vb*, *see* **draga**
drekka (drekkr; drakk, drukku; drukkinn) *vb* drink

drepa (drepr; drap, drápu; drepinn) *vb* kill; [*w dat*] put
drjúpa (drýpr; draup, drupu; dropit) *vb* drip
dró *vb*, *see* **draga**
dvelja (dvalð-) *vb* delay, defer; *refl* **dveljask** stay
dvergr *m* dwarf
dýr *n* animal, beast
dældarmaðr *m* gentle, easy man
dœgr *n* a half day (twelve hours of day or night); a full day of 24 hours; **fjǫgurra (fimm) dœgra haf**, a sail of four (five) days; **sjau dœgra sigling** a sail of seven days
dœl *f* dale, hollow
dǫgum *m*, *see* **dagr**
Døkkálfr *m* 'Dark-Elf'
døkkr (-v-) *adj* dark

E

eða *conj* or
Edda *f* Edda (*literary work*); **Snorra Edda** 'Snorri's Edda', *The Prose Edda* written by Snorri Sturluson
ef *conj* if
efla (-d-) *vb* make, perform
egg (-j-) *f* edge
eggja (-að-) *vb* egg on, urge, incite
Egill *m* Egil (*personal name*)
eiga (á, eigu; átti; áttr) *vb* own, possess; be married to, have (relatives); **eiga eptir** leave behind; **sem hon átti ætt til** which was characteristic for her family
eigi *adv* not, no
Einarr *m* Einar (*personal name*)
einn (*f* ein, *n* eitt) *num* one; *adj* one, a certain; **einn hverr** one, a certain; **á einu hverju sumri** one summer; (*n* **eitt**) one thing, the same thing
einvaldskonungr *m* sole ruler, monarch
Eiríkr *m* Eirik (*personal name*)
eitt *num* (*n*), *see* **einn**
ek (*acc* mik, *dat* mér, *gen* mín) *pron* I
ekki *indef pron* (*n*), *see* **engi**; *as adv* not
eldask (-ld-) *refl vb* grow old
eldr *m* fire
Elfráðr *m* Alfred (*personal name*)
Ella *m* Ælla, King of Northumbria (*personal name*)
elli *f* old age
ellifu *num* eleven
ellri *comp adj* older (*see* **gamall**)
ellstr *superl adj* oldest (*see* **gamall**)
elska (-að-) *vb* love; be fond of
em *vb*, *see* **vera**
en *conj* but; and (on the other hand)
en *conj* than
endi *m* end
engi (*f* engi, *n* ekki; *gen m/n* enskis) *indef pron* no one, not one, no; (*pl*) none; (*after neg*) any; (*n* **ekki**) nothing
England *n* England
enn *adv* still, yet; further, moreover
enskis *indef pron*, *see* **engi**
eptir *prep* [*w acc*] after (*time*); [*w dat*] after, along with; according to; **þar eptir** accordingly, from this; **eiga eptir** leave behind; **spyrja eptir** ask about
eptir *adv* behind, left over
er *rel pron/adv* when; where; who, which, that; *conj* when; since; **þar er** where; **þá er** when
er, **ert**, **erum** *vb*, *see* **vera**
Erlingr *m* Erling (*personal name*)
es = **er**
eta (etr; át, átu; etinn) *vb* eat
etja (att-) *vb* [*w dat*] incite, egg on; etja hestum incite horses (to fight)
ey (*dat* ey/eyju, *gen* -jar; *pl* -jar) *f* island
eyða (-dd-) *vb* lay waste; spend up, squander; *refl* **eyðask** be squandered, come to naught
Eylimi *m* Eylimi (*personal name*); legendary king, father of Hjordis
eyra *n* ear
Eymundr *m* Eymund (*personal name*)
Eysteinn *m* Eystein (*personal name*)

F

faðir (*acc/dat/gen* fǫður; *pl* feðr, *dat* feðrum, *gen* feðra) *m* father
fagna (-að-) *vb* [*w dat*] welcome
fagr (*f* fǫgr, *n* fagrt; *comp* fegri, *superl* fegrstr) *adj* beautiful, fair, fine; **fagr álitum** beautiful (in appearance), handsome
falla (fellr; fell, fellu; fallinn) *vb* fall
fannsk *vb*, *see* **finna**
fara (ferr; fór, fóru; farinn) *vb* go, travel; fare; **var farinn** had travelled; **fara með fíflsku** commit folly; *refl* **farask** go (of events), turn out; perish
farar *f pl*, *see* **fǫr**
farmaðr *m* traveller, sea-farer
fá (fær; fekk, fengu; fenginn) *vb* get; [*w gen*] marry; **fá sér liðs** gather a band of men, get support
Fáfnir *m* Fafnir (*personal name*); son of Hreidmar who turns himself into a dragon
fár *adj* few
feðgar *m pl* father and son(s)
feginn *adj* glad, pleased
fegrð *f* beauty; **fegrð á hár (líki)** beauty of hair (body)
fegri *comp adj* more beautiful (*see* **fagr**)
fegrstr *superl adj* fairest, most beautiful (*see* **fagr**); **fegrst talaðr** most eloquent
fekk *vb*, *see* **fá**
fell *n* mountain
fell, **fellr** *vb*, *see* **falla**
ferð (*pl* -ir) *f* trip, journey
fé (*gen* fjár; *pl gen* fjá) *n* property, wealth, money; cattle; **auðigr at fé** wealthy
fimm *num* five
fimmtán *num* fifteen
fingr *m* finger
finna (finnr; fann, fundu; fundinn) *vb* find; *refl* **finnask** appear; **finnask á** appear; **þá er honum fannsk mikit um** whom he liked very much
Finnr *m* Finn (*personal name*)
finnskr *adj* Finnish
Firðir *m pl* the Fjords (*place name*)
fiskr *m* fish
fíflska *f* folly, foolishness; **fara með fíflsku** commit folly
fjórir (*f* fjórar, *n* fjǫgur, *all gen* fjǫgurra) *num* four
fjórtán *num* fourteen
fjǫgur, **fjǫgurra** *num*, *see* **fjórir**
fjǫldi *m* multitude
fjǫlkunnigr *adj* skilled in magic, 'much knowing'
fjǫlmenni *n* crowd
fjǫlmennr *adj* populous, with many people, well attended
fjǫr (-v-) *n* life
fjǫrðr (*dat* firði, *gen* fjarðar; *pl* firðir, *acc* fjǫrðu, *gen* fjarða) *m* fjord
Fjǫrðu, **Fjǫrðum** *m pl*, *see* **Firðir**
fjǫrlausn *f* ransom for one's life
fjǫrsegi *m* heart ('life-muscle')
flá (flær; fló, flógu; fleginn) *vb* flay, strip
fleiri *comp adj* more (*see* **margr**)
flestr *comp adj* most (*see* **margr**)
flytja (flutt-) *vb* convey, carry; deliver (an address), recite; **flytja til eyrna [e-m]** convey to the ears of [sb], inform [sb]
flýja (-ð-) to flee
formáli *m* 'fore-speech', foretelling
fors (*pl* -ar) *m* waterfall
forvitni *f* curiosity
fólk *n* people
fór, **fóru** *vb*, *see* **fara**
fóstbróðir *m* foster-brother
fóstr (*gen* -rs) *n* fostering, fosterage
fóstri *m* foster-father
fram *adv* forward, forth; **ganga vel fram** fight valiantly; **um fram** in addition
frauð *n* froth, juice (of roasted meat)
frá *prep* [*w dat*] from; about; **segja frá** relate, tell about
frá *adv* away, off; **ofan frá** below
fránn *adj* gleaming, flashing
Freyr *m* Frey (*mythological name*, one of the Vanir)
Freysgoði *m* 'Frey's Chief' (*nickname*)
frétt (*pl* -ir) *f* news
Frigg *f* Frigg, wife of Odin (*mythological name*)
fríðastr *superl adj*, *see* **fríðr**
fríðr (*n* frítt) *adj* beautiful, handsome, fine; **fríðr sýnum** fine in appearance

frjósa (frýss; fraus, frusu; frosinn) *vb* freeze
frægr *adj* famous
frœkn (*also* **frœkinn**) *adj* bold, daring, valiant
fugl *m* bird
fuglsrǫdd *f* bird's voice, speech of birds
fullr *adj* full
fullsteiktr *ppart* fully roasted (*from* **steikja**)
fundr (*gen* -ar; *pl* -ir) *m* meeting; audience
funi *m* flame
furða *f* wonder, marvel
fylking *f* battle array, the ranks of an army; battalion
fylla (-d-) *vb* fill
fyrir *prep* [*w acc*] before, in front of (*motion*); for, because of; [*w dat*] before, in front of (*location*); at the head of (leading); with; for, by; because of; **fyrir ... sakar** on account of, because of; **fyrir sér** of oneself; **fyrir sik** for oneself, on one's own behalf; **fyrir strauminum** with the current; **fyrir útan** [*w acc*] outside; out beyond; **fyrir því, at** because; **draga fyrir** draw beyond; **ráða fyrir** rule over
fyrr *adv* before, earlier; **fyrr en** *conj* before
fyrri *comp adj* former
fyrst *superl adv* first, earliest
fyrstr *superl adj* first, foremost
fœða (-dd-) *vb* feed
fœra (-ð-) *vb* bring, convey; send, deliver, give; take
fǫður *m, see* **faðir**
fǫr (*pl* farar) *f* journey

G

gaf *vb, see* **gefa**
gagn (*pl* gǫgn) *n* advantage, benefit, produce, revenue
galtar *m, see* **gǫltr**
gamall (*acc* gamlan, *f* gǫmul, *n* gamalt; *comp* ellri, *superl* ellstr) *adj* old
gaman *n* fun, amusement, pleasure; **gera gaman** entertain; **at gaman sé at** that it is amusing
gamli (*gen* -a) *m* old one (*nickname*) (*wk m nom sg of* **gamall**)
ganga (gengr; gekk, gengu; genginn) *vb* go, walk; go out, spread; **ganga af** leave off, be finished with; **ganga at [e-m]** attack [sb]; **ganga á hǫnd [e-m]** submit to [sb], go into [sb]'s service, become [sb]'s retainer; **ganga fyrir** go before; **ganga til** approach, go up to a thing; **ganga vel fram** fight valiantly; **ganga yfir [e-n]** befall, happen to [sb]
Gangleri *m* Gangleri (*personal name*)
garðr *m* fence, wall
gefa (gefr; gaf, gáfu; gefinn) *vb* give
gegnum (*also* **í gegnum**) *prep* [*w acc*] through
geirr *m* spear
gekk, **gengir**, **gengit**, **gengr** *vb, see* **ganga**
gera (-ð-) *vb* make, do, build; **gera brúðlaup til** marry; **gera gaman** entertain; *refl* **gerask** become
gert *ppart, see* **gera**
geta (getr; gat, gátu; getinn) *vb* get; [*w gen*] guess; **geta at eiga** get in marriage, marry; **geta til** suppose, surmise
Gimlé *n* Gimle (*place name*)
Gísli *m* Gisli (*personal name*)
gjald *n* (*usu in pl* gjǫld) tribute; payment; reward; compensation; wergild (blood money)
glepja (glapð-) *vb* confuse, confound
Glitnir *m* Glitnir (*place name*)
Gnitaheiðr (*gen* -ar) *f* Gnitaheath (*place name*), where Fafnir, as a dragon, lies upon great wealth
gnótt *f* abundance
gnyðja (gnudd-) *vb* grunt
goð *n* god, one of the pagan gods
goðagremi *f* wrath of the gods
goði *m* chief
goðkunnigr *adj* related to the gods
goðorð *n* chieftainship, rank and authority of a **goði**
góðr (*n* gott; *comp* betri, *superl* beztr) *adj* good; **góðr af** proud of
góðhestr *m* good (riding) horse
grafa (grefr; gróf, grófu; grafinn) *vb* dig
Gramr *m* Gram (*mythological name*),

name of Sigurd the Dragon Slayer's sword
granahár *n* whisker
grand *n* injury
Grani *m* Grani (*mythological name*), Sigurd the Dragon-Slayer's horse
gras *n* grass, plant, herb
gráliga *adv* maliciously
gráta (grætr; grét, grétu; grátinn) *vb* cry
greiða (-dd-) *vb* pay
gremi *f* wrath, anger
griðarof *n pl* breach of the peace, trucebreaking
grimmr *adj* grim, fierce, savage
gríss (*gen* -s; *pl* -ir) *m* young pig, piglet
grjót *n* stones (*collective*), rubble
Grjótgarðr *m* Grjotgard ('Stone-Fence') (*personal name*)
gróf *vb*, *see* **grafa**
Grœnland *n* Greenland
grœnn *adj* green
grǫf (*gen* grafar; *pl* grafir/grafar) *f* pit, ditch
grǫn (*gen* granar; *pl* granar) *f* lip
gull *n* gold
gullbaugr (*dat* gullbaug(i)) *m* gold ring
Gunnarr *m* Gunnar (*personal name*)
Gunnlaugr *m* Gunnlaug (*personal name*)
gǫfugligr *adj* magnificent
gǫfugr *adj* noble
gøgnum *var of* **gegnum**
gǫltr (*dat* gelti, *gen* galtar; *pl* geltir, *acc* gǫltu, *gen* galta) *m* boar, hog
gǫrla *adv* fully, quite
gǫrr (-v-) *adj* done; **at svá gǫrvu** thus, this being the case, as things stood
gørr *comp adv* more fully, clearly (*see* **gǫrva**); **at gørr** for certain
gørst *superl adv* more fully, clearly (*see* **gǫrva**)
gørt *var of* **gert** *ppart*, *see* **gera**
gǫrva (*comp* gørr, *superl* gørst) *adv* quite, clearly
gørviligstr *superl adj*, *see* **gørviligr**
gørviligr *adj* accomplished, capable, enterprising

H

haf (*pl* hǫf) *n* sea; **fjǫgurra** (**fimm**) **dœgra haf** a sail of four (five) days
hafa (hef(i)r, -ð-) *vb* have; hold, keep; take; **hafa [e-m] heim með sér** bring [sb] home with oneself; **nǫkkut hafask at** undertake ('have at') something
hafnar, **hafnir** *f*, *see* **hǫfn**
hafsbotn (*gen* -botns; *pl* -botnar) *m* gulf; the Arctic Ocean (*place name*)
hagr *m* state, condition
halda (heldr; helt, heldu; haldinn) *vb* [*w acc/dat*] hold, hold fast; hold on to, keep, retain; direct, hold on a course; *refl* **haldask** hold true, remain valid, stand
hamrammr *adj* fierce, furious in battle (*lit.* 'shape-mighty'; used of warriors who 'changed shape', i.e., went berserk)
hana *pron*, *see* **hon**
hanga (hengr/hangir; hékk, hengu/héngu, hanginn) *vb* hang
hann (*acc* hann, *dat* honum, *gen* hans; *pl* þeir) *pron* he
hans *poss pron* his
Haraldr *m* Harald (*personal name*)
harðdrœgr *adj* hard to handle
harðliga *adv* forcibly, harshly, severely; hard
harðr (*f* hǫrð, *n* hart) *adj* hard
Haukadalr (*dat* Haukadal(i)) *m* 'Hawks' Dale' (*place name*)
haust *n* fall
Hákon (*gen* -ar) *m* Hakon (*personal name*)
hálfa *f* region, part
hár *n* hair
hár *adj* tall, high; loud
Hár *m* Har ('High') (*mythological name*, pseudonym of Odin)
hárfagr *adj* fair-haired
hásæti *n* high-seat, throne
hátt *adv* loudly
Hávarðr *m* Havard (*personal name*)
hefði, **hefi**, **hefir**, **hefr** *vb*, *see* **hafa**
hefja (hefr; hóf, hófu; hafinn) *vb* raise; begin; **hefja upp bónorð** propose marriage
hefna (-d-) *vb* avenge

heiðr (*pl* -ar) *f* heath
heill *adj* healthy, well, 'hale'; whole
heim *adv* (to) home (*motion*)
heima *adv* at home (*location*)
heima *m*, *see* **heimr**
heimamaðr *m* servant, man belonging to a household
heimr *m* home, dwelling; land, region of the world; the world; **kringla heimsins** the globe, earth; **of alla heima** over the whole world
heita (heitir; hét, hétu; heitinn) *vb* be named, be called; promise
heldr (*superl* helzt) *comp adv* more, very, rather
heldi, **heldr**, **heldu** *vb*, *see* **halda**
Helgi *m* Helgi ('Holy') (*personal name*)
helgistaðr *m* holy place
helmingr *m* half; **skipta í helminga** divide into two equal portions
helzk *vb*, *see* **halda**
helzt *superl adv* especially; **allra helzt** especially, most of all
hendi *f*, *see* **hǫnd**
hengu (*inf* **hanga**) *vb* (they) hung
hennar *poss pron* her, hers
herfǫr *f* military expedition
herja (-að-) *vb* raid, harry; ravage, plunder
herkonungr *m* warrior-king
herr (*gen* -jar; *pl* -jar) *m* army, host
herra *m* master, lord
hersaga *f* war-tidings, news of war (*see also* **herr**, **saga**)
hersir *m* local chieftain; a military leader with power from a king
hersǫgu *f*, *see* **hersaga**
hestaat *n* horse fight
hestavít *n* horse fight
hestr *m* horse, stallion
heyra (-ð-) *vb* hear
hégómi *m* insincerity
hér *adv* here
hét *vb*, *see* **heita**
Hildigunnr *f* Hildigunn (*personal name*)
Himinbjǫrg *n pl* 'Heaven Mountains' (*place name*)
himinn *m* heaven; **á himni** in heaven
hinn *art*, *var of* **inn**
hinn *pron* this (the other)
hitta (-tt-) *vb* meet; *refl* **hittask** meet one another
hjarta (*pl* hjǫrtu, *gen* hjartna) *n* heart
hjartablóð *n* heart's blood
hjá *prep* [*w dat*] with, by, beside
hjálmr *m* helmet
Hjálprekr *m* Hjalprek (*personal name*), a legendary king
hjó *vb*, *see* **hǫggva**
Hjǫrdís *f* Hjordis (*personal name*); mother of Sigurd
Hjǫrleifr *m* Hjorleif (*personal name*)
hjǫrtr (*dat* hirti, *gen* hjartar; *pl* hirtir, *acc* hjǫrtu) *m* deer, stag, hart
Hjǫrtr (*dat* Hirti, *gen* Hjartar) *m* Hjort ('Deer') (*personal name*)
hlaup *n* leap, jump
hlaupa (hleypr; hljóp, hljópu; hlaupinn) *vb* run
Hliðskjálf *f* Hlidskjalf, name of Odin's throne
Hlíðarendi *m* Hlidarendi, a farm in southern Iceland (*place name*)
hlíf (*pl* -ar) *f* cover, protection (esp. of a shield or armor)
hluti *m* part
hlutr (*dat* hlut, *gen* -ar; *pl* -ir) *m* part; **um alla hluti** in all respects
hlýða (-dd-) [*w dat*] *vb* listen to; **hlýða til** listen to
hlæja (hlær; hló, hlógu; hleginn) *vb* laugh
hof *n* temple
Hof *n* Hof ('Temple') (*place name*)
Hofsland *n* the Hof estate
hon (*acc* hana, *dat* henni, *gen* hennar; *pl* þær) *pron* she
honum *pron*, *see* **hann**
horfa (-ð-) *vb* look, (turn so as to) look on; **horfa á** look at; **horfask til** be in prospect
horn *n* horn
Horn *n* Horn, farm in Southeastern Iceland, one of the first settlements in Iceland (*place name*)
hóf *vb*, *see* **hefja**
hófsmaðr *m* man of moderation and restraint
hógværr *adj* gentle, quiet
Hrafn *m* Hrafn ('Raven') (*personal name*)
Hrafnkell *m* Hrafnkel (*personal name*)
hraustr *adj* bold

Hreiðmarr *m* Hreidmar (*mythological name*), father of Otr, Fafnir, and Regin
hrím *n* hoar-frost, rime
hrímsteinn *m* rime-stone
hringr *m* ring
hross *n* horse, mare
Hrotti *m* Hrotti (*mythological name*), name of a sword
Hróaldr *m* Hroald (*personal name*)
Hróðgeirr *m* Hrodgeir (*personal name*)
hrósa (-að-) *vb* [*w dat*] boast (of)
hræða (-dd-) *vb* [*w acc*] frighten; *refl* **hræðask** be frightened; **hræðask [e-t]** be afraid of [sth]
hugða, **hugði** *vb, see* **hyggja**
hugr (*dat* hug(i), *gen* -ar; *pl* -ir) *m* mind; mood; courage; **vera í hug [e-m]** be in [sb]'s mind
hulði, **huldr** *vb, see* **hylja**
hundrað (*pl* hundruð) *n* hundred
hús *n* house
hvar *int adv* where
hvarf *n* disappearance
Hvarf *n* 'Disappearance', Cape Farewell in Greenland (*place name*)
hvass (*f* hvǫss, *n* hvas(s)t) *adj* sharp, keen
hvat *n int pron* what; *rel pron* what, that which (*see* **hverr**)
hvárr *int pron* who, which (of two); *indef pron* each (of two)
hvárrtveggja *indef pron* each (of two)
hvárt *conj* whether
hváta *vb* stick (in), poke, pierce
hverr (*n* hvat, *acc m* hvern; -j-) *int pron* who, what, which; **af hverju** why, for what reason; *indef pron* each, any(one), every(one); **einn hverr** one, a certain
hversu *adv* how; **hversu lízk þér á** how do you like
hvert *adv* to where
hvetja (hvatt-) *vb* whet, sharpen
hvé *adv* how, to what extent
hví *adv* why, for what reason (*n dat of* **hvat**)
hvítr *adj* white
Hvítserkr *m* Hvitserk ('White-Shirt') (*personal name*)
hyggja (hugð-) *vb* think; **hyggja at** pay attention to, consider
hylja (huld/hulð-) *vb* hide, cover
Hœnir *m* Hœnir (*mythological name*), one of the Æsir
hǫf *n pl, see* **haf**
hǫfðingi *m* leader
hǫfðu *vb, see* **hafa**
hǫfn (*gen* hafnar; *pl* hafnir) *f* harbor
hǫfuð *n* head
hǫfuðsbani *m* death, destruction
hǫfuðstaðr *m* capital, chief place
hǫgg (-v-) *n* stroke, blow
hǫggva (høggr; hjó, hjoggu; hǫgg(v)inn) *vb* strike, hack, hew
hǫnd (*dat* hendi, *gen* handar; *pl* hendr) *f* hand; **ganga á hǫnd [e-m]** submit to [sb], go into [sb]'s service, become [sb]'s retainer; **ór hendi þér** out of your hand; **selja í hendr** turn over; **taka hǫndum** take hold of, seize with the hands
Hǫrðakonungr *m* king of Hǫrðaland (in Western Norway)

I

igða *f* nuthatch (species of bird)
illa (*comp* verr, *superl* verst) *adv* badly, 'ill'
illr (*comp* verri, *superl* verstr) *adj* bad, evil, 'ill'
Ingi *m* Ingi (*personal name*)
Ingibjǫrg *f* Ingibjorg (*personal name*)
inn (*f* in, *n* it) *art* the
inn *adv* in (*motion*); **inn í** into
innlenzkr *adj* native
it *art* (*n*), *see* **inn**

Í

í *prep* [*w acc*] in, into (*motion*); [*w dat*] in, within; at (*location*); **í þann tíma** at that time
Írland *n* Ireland
Ísland *n* Iceland
íslenzkr *adj* Icelandic
Ívarr *m* Ivar (*personal name*)

íþrótt (*pl* -ir) *f* skill, feat, accomplishment

J

jafna (-að-) *vb* compare, liken; **jafna til** compare with, liken to
jafningi (*pl* -jar) *m* equal, match
jalda *f poet* mare
jarl *m* earl
Játvarðr *m* Edward (*personal name*)
Jórsalaland *n* 'Jerusaem's Land', Israel (*place name*)
Jǫlduhlaup *n* 'Mare's Leap', Slyne Head in Ireland (*place name*)
jǫrð (*dat* -u) *f* earth
jǫtunn *m* giant
Jǫtunheimar *m pl* Land of Giants

K

kalla (-að-) *vb* call, name
kanna (-að-) *vb* search, explore
kannt *vb, see* **kunna**
kapalhestr *m* packhorse
kapítuli *m* chapter
kappi *m* hero, champion, great fighter
kasta (-að-) *vb* [*w dat*] throw, cast; **kasta boganum** throw the bow
kastali *m* castle
kaupa (keypt-) *vb* buy
kemr *vb, see* **koma**
kjósa (kýss; kaus/kǫri, kusu/kuru, kosinn/kørinn) *vb* choose
Kerlingardalsá *f* 'River of the Valley of the Old Woman' (*place name*)
klauf *vb, see* **kljúfa**
kljúfa (klýfr; klauf, klufu; klofinn) *vb* split, cleave
klyf (*pl* -jar) *f* pack (for a horse)
klæði *n* cloth; garment, clothing
knǫrr (*acc* knǫrr, *dat* knerri, *gen* knarrar; *pl* knerrir, *acc* knǫrru, *dat* knǫrrum,) *m* ship; merchant vessel
Kolskeggr *m* Kolskegg (*personal name*)
koma (kemr; kom, kómu; kominn) *vb* come; *refl* **komask** reach, arrive; **koma at** arrive; **koma á** strike; **koma upp** come about, happen; **komask undan** escape
komsk *vb, see* **koma**
kona (*pl gen* kvenna) *f* woman, wife; **biðja konu** ask for a woman in marriage
konar *gen sg of obs* ***konr** *m* kind, sort; **alls konar** of every kind, of all kinds
konungr *m* king
konungsson *m* prince
kostr (*gen* -ar; *pl* -ir) *m* choice, alternative; opportunity; **at ǫðrum kosti** otherwise
kómu *vb, see* **koma**
krapparúm *n* bow-room (on a ship)
kringla *f* disk, circle, orb; **kringla heimsins** the globe, earth
kunna (kann, kunnu; kunni; kunnat) *vb* know, understand; be able
kunnigr *adj* known; knowing, skilled in magic
kvað *vb, see* **kveða**
kvaddi *vb, see* **kveðja**
kváðu, kváðusk *vb, see* **kveða**
kveða (kveðr; kvað, kváðu; kveðinn) *vb* say; **kveða á** fix, determine; *refl* **kveðask** say of oneself [*w inf*]
kveðja (kvadd-) *vb* greet
kveld *n* evening
Kveld-Úlfr *m* Kveld-Ulf ('Evening-Wolf') (*personal name*)
kvikvendi *n pl* living creatures, animals, beasts
Kvígandafell *n* 'Heifer Mountain' (*place name*)
kyrr *adj* still, quiet
kýr (*acc/dat* kú, *gen* kýr; *pl nom/acc* kýr, *dat* kúm, *gen* kúa) *f* cow
kǫllum *vb, see* **kalla**
kærleikr *m* friendly terms
kærr *adj* dear; **kærr at** fond of
kœmi *vb, see* **koma**

L

lagabrot *n* lawbreaking; **lagabrot landsréttar** breaking the law of the land

lagði, lagðisk *vb, see* **leggja**

lagðr *m* tuft (of wool or hair)

lagt *vb, see* **leggja**

land (*pl* lǫnd) *n* land

landnám *n* settlement, 'land taking'

Landnámabók *f* Book of Settlements

landsréttr *m* law of the land; **lagabrot landsréttar** breaking the law of the land

Langanes *n* Langanes ('Long Headland'), peninsula in Northeast Iceland (*place name*)

langfeðgar *m pl* forefathers, ancestors (through the father's line)

langr *adj* long

langt *adv* far

lausn (*gen* -ar; *pl* -ir) *f* ransom

lauss *adj* free

laust *n adj, see* **lauss**

laust *vb, see* **ljósta**

lax (*gen* lax; *pl* laxar) *m* salmon

lá *vb, see* **liggja**

láta (lætr; lét, létu; látinn) *vb* let, allow; let go, lose; put, place, set; [*w inf*] have something done; **láta fram** let go, yield, hand over; **láta lífit** lose one's life; *refl* **látask** declare (of oneself)

leggja (lagð-) *vb* lay, place; set, fix, arrange; [*w dat*] stab, thrust; **leggja [e-t] á [e-n]** impose, lay [sth] upon [sb]; **leggja [e-u] í gegnum [e-n]** thrust [sth] through [sb]; **leggja til (orð)** say; **leggja við** accuse of, declare guilty of or subject to; *refl* **leggjask** lay oneself, lie down; **leggjask at sofa** go to sleep

leggr (*gen* -jar; *pl* -ir) *m* leg, limb; hollow bone (of arm and leg)

leið (*pl* -ir) *f* way; path, road

leit *vb, see* **líta**

leita (-að-) *vb* [*w gen*] seek, search for

lemja (lamd-) *vb* beat, thrash

lendr *adj* 'landed', having lands; **lendr maðr** 'landed man' (Norw *lendmann*), a Norwegian nobleman whose lands and income were granted by the king

lengi *adv* long, a long time

lengja (-d-) *vb* lengthen

lengra *comp adv* farther

lét, lézk *vb, see* **láta**

lið *n* troop, force, band of armed supporters; aid, assistance; **fá sér liðs** gather a band of men, get support

liðfœrr *adj* able-bodied

lifa (-ð-) *vb* live; **lifa við** live on, feed on

liggja (liggr; lá, lágu, leginn) *vb* lie

litlu *adv* a little (*n dat sg of* **lítill**); **litlu síðar** a little later

líf *n* life; **á lífi** alive

líki *n* form, shape, likeness; body

líkligr *adj* likely, probable; **sem líkligt er** as might be expected

líknsamr *adj* gracious, merciful

líta (lítr; leit, litu; litinn) *vb* look; **líta á** look at, consider; **hversu lízk þér á** how do you like

lítill (*f* lítil, *n* lítit; *acc m* litlan, *f* litla, *dat m* litlum, *n* litlu; *pl* litlir, etc.; *comp* minni, *superl* minnstr) *adj* little, small

lítt (*comp* minnr, *superl* minnst) *adv* little

Ljósálfr *m* 'Light-Elf'

ljóss *adj* light, fair; clear

ljósta (lýstr; laust, lustu; lostinn) *vb* strike, hit

loðbrók *f* 'Hairy-Breeches' (*nickname*)

lofa (-að-) *vb* praise

Loki *m* Loki (*mythological name*), the trickster god, one of the Æsir

lokit *ppart, see* **lúka**

lunga *n* lung

lúka (lýkr; lauk, luku; lokinn) *vb* [*w dat*] end, finish

lýsa (-t-) *vb* shine

lætr *vb, see* **láta**

lǫg *n pl* law(s)

lǫgmaðr *m* lawman, lawyer

M

maðr (*acc* mann, *dat* manni, *gen* manns; *pl nom/acc* menn, *dat* mǫnnum, *gen* manna) *m* man; person, human being; **hvat manna** what sort of man
Magnús *m* Magnus (*personal name*)
man *vb, see* **muna**
mann, **manna**, **manns** *m, see* **maðr**
mannfólk *n* mankind, humanity
mannraun *f* trial (of courage), danger, peril; adversity
mannvænn *adj* promising
margr (*f* mǫrg, *n* mar(g)t; *comp* fleiri, *superl* flestr) *adj* [*w sg*] many a (in collective sense); [*w pl*] many; **mǫrgu sinni** many a time, on many occasions
marka (-að-) *vb* notice; infer
má *vb, see* **mega**
mál *n* speech, language; case, matter, affair
málmr *m* ore; metal
mátt, **mátti** *vb, see* **mega**
með *prep* [*w acc*] with (bringing, carrying along, or forcing); [*w dat*] with (accompanying or being together); along; with, by, using; between; **upp með** up along
meðan *conj* while
mega (má, megu; mátti; mátt) *vb* be able, be allowed; **vera má þat** maybe
mein *n* hurt, harm; **verða [e-m] at meini** cause [sb] harm
meir(r) *comp adv* more (*see* **mjǫk**)
meiri *comp adj* greater (*see* **mikill**)
menn *m pl, see* **maðr**
mest *superl adv* most (*see* **mjǫk**); **sem mest** as much as possible
mestr *superl adj* greatest; most (*see* **mikill**)
metnaðarmaðr *m* man of ambition
mey, **meyjar** *f, see* **mær**
mér *pron, see* **ek**
miðla (-að-) *vb* share
miðr (-j-) *adj* middle; **boga Einars miðjan** to the middle of Einars bow
mik *pron, see* **ek**
mikill (*f* mikil, *n* mikit, *acc m* mikinn; *comp* meiri, *superl* mestr) *adj* big, large, great; much; (of rivers) swollen, running high; **mikill fyrir sér** strong, powerful, mighty
mikit *adv* much (*see* **mikill**)
miklu *adv* [*w comp*] much (*n dat sg of* **mikill**)
milli *prep* [*w gen*] between; **standa milli** separate, set at odds
minn (*f* mín, *n* mitt; *acc m* minn, *f* mína, *dat m* mínum, *n* mínu, *gen m/n* míns; *pl m* mínir, *f* mínar, *n* mín, *acc m* mína, *dat* mínum) *poss adj* my, mine
minni *comp adj* littler, smaller, lesser (*see* **lítill**)
minnr *comp adv* less (*see* **lítt**)
minnst *superl adv* least (*see* **lítt**)
minnstr *superl adj* littlest, smallest, least (*see* **lítill**)
mín *pron, see* **ek**
mjólk *f* milk
mjólk-á *f* milk-stream, river of milk
mjǫk (*comp* meir(r), *superl* mest) *adv* much, greatly, very; almost
móðir (*acc/dat/gen* móður; *pl* mœðr, *dat* mœðr, *gen* mœðra) *f* mother
móti *prep* [*w dat*] toward, against
muna (man, muna; mundi; munaðr) *vb* remember
munnr *m* mouth
munu (mun, munu; mundi; *pret inf* mundu) *vb* will, shall (*future*), be likely
mylja (muld-) *vb* crush to pieces
myndi *vb, see* **munu**
mæla (-t-) *vb* say, speak; **mæla við** say to, speak to
mær (*acc* mey, *dat* meyju, *gen* meyjar; *pl nom/acc* meyjar, *dat* meyjum, *gen* meyja) *f* girl, maiden
mǫgr (*dat* megi, *gen* magar; *pl* megir, *acc* mǫgu) *m* boy, youth

N

nafn (*pl* nǫfn) *n* name
nakkvat *var of* **nǫkkut** (*see* **nǫkkurr**)
nam *vb, see* **nema**
nauð *f* need

nauðgjald *n* forced payment
ná (-ð-) *vb* [*w dat*] reach, attain
nábúi *m* neighbor
nám *n* acquisition, occupation; **landnám** land-taking, settlement
nár (*gen* -s; *pl* -ir, *dat* nám) *m* corpse, dead man
nátt *var of* **nótt**
náttstaðr *m* night-quarters, lodging for the night
nefna (-d-) *vb* name, call; mention by name
neinn (= **né einn**) (*n* neitt) *indef pron* no, not one; [*w neg*] (not ...) any
neitt *indef pron, see* **neinn**
nema *conj* but (that), except
nema (nemr; nam, námu; numinn) *vb* take; **nema á brott** abduct
nes (-j-) *n* headland, peninsula
neyta (-tt-) *vb* [*w gen*] use, make use of
né *conj* nor
niðr *adv* down; **setja niðr** settle (a dispute)
niðri *adv* down (in)
nítján *num* nineteen
níu *num* nine
Njáll *m* Njal (*personal name*)
norðanverðr *adj* northern
norðr *adv* north
norðrhálfa *f* northern region
Norðrlǫnd *n pl* Northern Lands (Northern Europe) (*place name*)
norn *f* Norn
Nóregr *m* Norway
nótt (*gen* nætr; *pl* nætr) *f* night
nú *adv* now
nær *prep* [*w dat*] near
nær *adv* near, nearly
nær *conj* when
næst *adv* next (following); **því næst** then, next, thereupon
nǫkkurr (*f* nǫkkur, *n* nǫkkut) *indef pron* any, anyone; some, someone; one, a certain; (*n*) anything, something
nǫkkut *n adj as adv* somewhat, in some degree (*see* **nǫkkurr**); **nǫkkut hafask at** undertake ('have at') something; **vera nǫkkut við** be somehow connected with
Nǫrvasund *n pl* the Straits of Gibraltar (*place name*)
Nǫrvi *m* Norvi (*personal name*)

O

oddr *m* point
of *adv* too
of *prep* [*w acc/dat*] over (*distance*); for, during (*time*)
ofan *adv* down, from above; **ofan frá** below
ok *conj* and (in addition); as
okkarr *poss adj* our (two); **okkrum mundi þykkja** it would seem to us
okkr *pron, see* **vit**
opt *adv* often
orð *n* word
orðinn *ppart, see* **verða**
ormr *m* snake, serpent
ormslíki *n* form of a snake
Ormstunga *f* 'Serpent's Tongue' (*nickname*)
orrosta *f* battle
oss *pron, see* **vér**
otr (*gen* -rs; *pl* -rar) *m* otter
Otr *m* Otr (*mythological name*), Otter, son of Hreidmar
otrbelgr *m* otter skin
otrgjǫld *n pl* otter's ransom, wergild (blood money) for a dead otter
oxi (*pl* øxn) *m* ox

Ó

ó- (*also* **ú-**) *pref* un-, in-
Óðinn *m* Odin (*mythological name*), chief god of the Æsir
ójafnaðr (*gen* -ar) *m* injustice; unfairness
ójafnaðarmaðr *m* unjust man, quarrelsome and overbearing, difficult to deal with
Óláfr *m* Olaf (*personal name*)
ólíkligr *adj* unlikely
ólíkr *adj* unlike, different; **ólíkr**

sýnum different in appearance; **ólíkari reyndum** more different in reality
ór (*also* **úr**) *prep* [*w dat*] out of, from; **ór hendi þér** out of your hands
óráð *n* evil plan, ill-advised plan
óreyndr *adj* unproved
ósáttr *adj* unreconciled, at odds
ótiginn *adj* not noble (of family), of common descent
óttask (-að-) *refl vb* fear
óvinr (*gen* -ar; *pl* -ir) *m* enemy
óœðri *comp adj* lower

P

penningr *m* penny, coin

R

Ragnarr *m* Ragnar (*personal name*)
rak *vb, see* **reka**
Randalín *f* Randalin (*personal name*)
rangr (*f* rǫng) *adj* wrong; crooked
rani *m* snout
rann *vb, see* **renna**
rauðavíkingr *m* 'red' viking, a particularly fierce and violent viking
rauðr *adj* red
ráð *n* counsel, advice, plan; match, marriage; **synja ráðs** refuse a proposal of marriage; **taka til ráða** adopt a plan
ráða (ræðr; réð, réðu; ráðinn) *vb* [*w dat*] advise, counsel; decide, determine; control, rule, govern; prevail in; **ráða fyrir** rule over; **ráða um við [e-n]** consult with [sb]; **þá er eigi ráðit** then there is no help for
Refill *m* Refil (*mythological name*), name of a sword
Refr *m* Ref ('Fox') (*personal name*)
Reginn *m* Regin (*mythological name*), son of Hreidmar and foster-father of Sigurd
reið *vb, see* **ríða**
reiði *f* anger
reiðr (*n* reitt) *adj* angry, wrathful
reka (rekr; rak, ráku; rekinn) *vb* be carried along, drift; **reka fyrir strauminum** drift with the current
renna (rennr; rann, runnu; runninn) *vb* run, flow
Reykjanes *n* Reykjanes ('Smoky Headland'), peninsula in Southwest Iceland (*place name*)
reykr (*gen* -jar; *pl* -ir) *m* smoke, steam
reyna (-d-) *vb* try, prove; experience; **reyna með** put to the test
reynd *f* experience; **reyndum** in reality
réð *vb, see* **ráða**
rétt *adv* straight (*see* **réttr**)
réttlátr *adj* just
réttr *adj* straight; right, just
ríða (ríðr; reið, riðu; riðinn) *vb* ride, go on horseback [*w dat of animal, acc of road or place*]; **ríða hesti** ride a horse; **ríða leið sína** ride on one's way
ríkr *adj* powerful, mighty
ríki *n* realm, kingdom; power; **setja til ríkis** put in power
rísa (ríss, reis, risu, risinn) *vb* rise
róg *f* stife, discord
rógmálmr *m* metal of strife
runnu *vb, see* **renna**
rýrr *adj* thin
ræðr *vb, see* **ráða**
rǫdd (*gen* raddar; *pl* raddir) *f* voice
Rǫgnvaldr *m* Rognvald (*personal name*)
rǫnum *m, see* **rani**

S

saga *f* story
sagði, **sagt** *vb, see* **segja**
salr (*dat* sal, *gen* -ar; *pl* -ir) *m* room, hall
saltr *adj* salt(y)
saman *adv* together; **bera saman** collect, gather together
samr *adj* same

sá (*f* sú, *n* þat; *acc* þann, *dat* þeim, *gen* þess; *pl* þeir) *dem pron/adj* that (one)
sá *vb, see* **sjá**
sár *n* wound
sátu *vb, see* **sitja**
segi *m* slice, strip, shred
segja (sagð-) *vb* say, tell; **segja frá** relate, tell about; **segja til** tell, inform of
seinþreyttr *adj* slow to stir up; **seinþreyttr til vandræða** slow to be drawn into a quarrel
selagnúpr *m* 'Seal-Cliff' (*nickname*)
selja (-d-) *vb* deliver, hand over; **selja í hendr** turn over (to)
sem *rel pron* who, which, that; *conj* as; [*w subjunct*] as if; [*w superl*] as ... as possible; **sem mest** as much as possible; **sem skjótast** at once, as soon as possible; **þar sem** there where
senda (-nd-) *vb* send
serkr (*gen* -s/jar; *pl* -ir, *gen* -ja) *m* shirt
setja (-tt-) *vb* set, put, place; **setja [e-n] fyrir** order [sb] to keep watch; **setja niðr** settle (a dispute); **setja til ríkis** put in power; *refl* **setjask** settle oneself, sit down
sex *num* six; **sex tigir** *num* [*w gen*] sixty
sextán *num* sixteen
sé *vb, see* **vera**
sér *refl pron, see* **sik**
sér *vb, see* **sjá**
sigla (-d-) *vb* sail
sigling (*pl* -ar) *f* sailing; voyage by sail; **sjau dœgra sigling** a sail of seven days
sigra (-að-) *vb* conquer, vanquish, be victorious, overcome; *refl* **sigrask** gain victory
Sigríðr *f* Sigrid (*personal name*)
sigrsæll *adj* victorious
sigrumsk *vb, see* **sigra**
Sigmundr (*gen* -ar) *m* Sigmund (*personal name*); son of Volsung and father of Sigurd
Sigurðr (*gen* -ar) *m* Sigurd (*personal name*); legendary hero who slays Fafnir the dragon
sik (*dat* sér, *gen* sín) *refl pron* him-/her-/it-/oneself, themselves
silfr *n* silver
sinn *n* a time, instance, occasion; **mǫrgu sinni** many a time, on many occasions
sinn (*f* sín, *n* sitt; *acc m* sinn, *f* sína, *dat m* sínum, *n* sínu, *gen m/n* síns; *pl m* sínir, *f* sínar, *n* sín, *acc m* sína, *dat* sínum) *refl poss adj* his, her, its, their (own)
sitja (sitr; sat, sátu; setinn) *vb* sit
sitt *refl poss adj* (*n*), *see* **sinn**
síð *adv* late
síðan *adv* then, later, afterwards, after that
síðar *comp adv* later (*see* **síð**)
síðr *comp adv* less; **þótt ek ætla þat síðr mun vera** although I think that is less likely
sín, **sína**, **síns**, **sínum** *refl poss adj, see* **sinn**
sín *refl pron, see* **sik**
Síreksstaðir *m pl* Sireksstadir ('Sirek's Farmstead') (*place name*)
sjau *num* seven; **sjau tigir** *num* [*w gen*] seventy
sjautján *num* seventeen
sjá (= **þessi**) *dem pron/adj* this (one)
sjá (sér; sá, sá; sénn) *vb* see
sjálfr *adj* self, him-/her-/it-/oneself, themselves
sjóða (sýðr; sauð, suðu; soðinn) *vb* boil, 'seethe'
sjón *f* sight, eyesight
sjóni *m* 'The Seer' (*nickname*)
sjónlítill *adj* having poor eyesight
skal *vb, see* **skulu**
Skalla-Grímr *m* Skalla-Grim (*personal name*)
skammr (*f* skǫmm, *n* skam(m)t; *comp* skem(m)ri, *superl* skem(m)str) *adj* short, brief
skapa (-að-) *vb* shape, form
skarpr *adj* sharp
skaut *vb, see* **skjóta**
skáld *n* poet, 'skald'
Skáldskaparmál *n pl* 'Poetic Diction', the second section of *The Prose Edda*
skáldskapr (*gen* -ar; *pl* -ir) *m* poetry, 'skaldship'
skemmstr *superl adj, see* **skammr**
skemmtiliga *adv* entertainingly
skera (skerr; skar, skáru; skorinn) *v*

cut, carve, 'shear'
skilja (-d-) *vb* part, divide, separate; discern, understand; *refl* **skiljask** part
skildi, skildir *m, see* **skjǫldr**
skilnaðr *m* parting
skip *n* ship
skipakostr *m* naval force
skipta (-pt-) *vb* [*w dat*] divide, share; **skipta í helminga** divide into two equal portions
skína (skínn; skein, skinu; skininn) *vb* shine
skírr *adj* pure
skírskota (-að-) *vb* refer to, appeal to; **skírskota ek undir þik** I call you to witness
skjóta (skýtr; skaut, skutu; skotinn) *vb* shoot; **skjóta af** shoot with
skjǫldr (*dat* skildi, *gen* skjaldar; *pl* skildir, *acc* skjǫldu, *gen* skjalda) *m* shield
skotit *ppart, see* **skjóta**
skógr (*gen* -ar; *pl* -ar) *m* forest, woods
skór (*dat* skó, *gen* skós; *pl* skúar, *acc/gen* skúa, *dat* skóm) *m* shoe
skreið *vb, see* **skríða**
skríða (skríðr; skreið, skriðu; skriðinn) *vb* crawl, creep
Skuld *f* Skuld ('Debt'), one of the Norns
skulu (skal, skulu; skyldi; *pret inf* skyldu) *vb* shall (necessity); must
skúa *m, see* **skór**
skúta *f* small boat, skiff
skyldi, skyldu *vb, see* **skulu**
skǫmm *f* shame
sleikja (-t-) *vb* lick
slíkr *adj* such
smár *adj* small
smiðr *m* smith
smíða (-að-) *vb* work in wood or metals, make, build
smyrja (smurð-) *vb* anoint, 'smear'
smæri *comp adj* smaller (*see* **smár**)
snemma (*also* **snimma**) (*comp* snemr, *superl* snemst) *adv* early, soon
sneri, sneru *vb, see* **snúa**
Snorri *m* Snorri (*personal name*); Snorri Sturluson, author of *The Prose Edda*
snúa (snýr; snøri/sneri; snúinn) *vb* turn; *refl* **snúask** turn oneself
snær (*gen* snævar/snæfar) *m* snow
Snæfellsnes *n* Snæfellsnes ('Snow Mountain's Headland'), peninsula in Western Iceland (*place name*)
sofa (sefr; svaf, sváfu; sofinn) *vb* sleep
sogit *ppart, see* **súga**
Sogn *n* Sogn, area in Western Norway (*place name*)
Sólundir *pl* Solundir, islands off Sogn in Western Norway (*place name*)
sonargjǫld *n pl* ransom, wergild (blood money) for a son
sonr (*dat* syni, *gen* sonar; *pl* synir, *acc* syni/sonu) *m* son
sól *f* sun
spakr *adj* wise
spekingr *m* wise man, sage
speni *m* teat
spilla (-t-) *vb* [*w dat*] spoil, destroy
spillir *m* spoiler; **spillir bauga** *poet* generous lord, spoiler (= distributor) of rings
spjót *n* spear
spurði, spurðr *ppart, see* **spyrja**
spyrja (spurð-) *vb* ask; **spyrja eptir** ask about
spýja (spýr; spjó, spjó; spúinn) *vb* spew
staddr *adj* present; placed, situated
staðr (*gen* -ar; *pl* -ir) *m* place; stead, parcel of land
Staðr (*gen* -ar) *m* Stad, a peninsula in Western Norway (*place name*)
stakkr *m* haystack
standa (stendr; stóð, stóðu; staðinn) *vb* stand, be located; **standa milli** separate, set at odds; **standa við** withstand
Stangarhǫgg *n* Staff-Struck (*nick-name*)
Starkaðr *m* Starkad (*personal name*)
steði (-ja) *m* anvil
steðr *f pl, see* **stoð**
steig *vb, see* **stíga**
steikja (-t/ð-) *vb* roast
Steinarr *m* Steinar (*personal name*)
Steinbjǫrn *m* Steinbjorn ('Stone-Bear') (*personal name*)
steinn *m* stone; stone dwelling, cave
sterkr *adj* strong; **sterkr at afli** strong
stilla (-lt-) *vb* restrain, calm, still
stilltr *adj* calm, composed

stíga (stígr; steig/sté, stigu; stiginn) *vb* step (up); **stíga á bak** mount on horseback
stoð (*pl* steðr) *f* pillar
stokkinn *ppart* spattered, stained (*esp* with blood) (*from* **støkkva**)
stokkr *m* stock of an anvil
stóð, **stóðu** *vb*, *see* **standa**
stóll *m* chair
stólpi *m* post
stórlyndr *adj* magnanimous
stórr *adj* big, great, important
stórráðr *adj* ambitious
stórskip *n* large ship
straumr *m* stream, current
stund (*dat* -u; *pl* -ir) *f* length of time, a while
stundum *adv* sometimes (*dat pl of* **stund**); **stundum… stundum…** sometimes… at other times…
Sturlubók *f* 'Sturla's Book', version of the **Landámabók** made by Sturla Thordarson
stýra (-ð-) *vb* [*w dat*] steer; rule, govern
støkkva (støkkr; stǫkk, stukku; stokkinn) *vb* spring, burst, leap; be sprinkled, spattered
stǫng (*gen* stangar; *pl* stangir/stengr) *f* pole, staff
suðr (*gen* suðrs) *n* the south; *adv* southwards; **í suðr** south(wards)
Suðrríki *n* Southern Realm (Southern Europe) (*place name*)
sumar (*dat* sumri) *n* summer
sumr *adj* some
sundr (*also* **í sundr**) *adv* apart, asunder
sunna *f* sun
sunnan *adv* from the south; on the south side; **fyrir sunnan** [*w acc*] to the south of
sunnanverðr *adj* southern; **á sunnanverðum enda** on the southern end
Sunnudalr (*dat* Sunnudal(i)) *m* Sunnudal ('Sun Dale') (*place name*)
sú (*acc* þá, *dat* þeiri, *gen* þeirar; *pl* þær) *dem pron/adj* (*f*), that (one) (*see* **sá**)
súga (sýgr; saug/só, sugum; soginn) *vb* suck
Súrr *m* Sur (*personal name*)
Svalbarði *m* Svalbard ('Cold Coast'), archipelago in the Arctic Ocean (*place name*)
svalr *adj* cool, fresh
svara (-að-) *vb* [*w dat*] answer, reply
svardagi *m* oath
Svartálfar *m pl* black elves
Svartálfheimr *m* world of the black elves
svartr (*f* svǫrt, *n* svart) *adj* black
svá *adv* so, thus, in this way; such; **svá … at** so … that; **ok svá** and also
sváfu *vb*, *see* **sofa**
sveigja (-ð-) *vb* bend; **sveigja at** deal with harshly
svelgja (svelgr; svalg, sulgu; sólginn) *vb* swallow
sveinn *m* boy, lad
sveiti *m* sweat; blood
sverð *n* sword
sverðsegg (-j-) *f* sword's edge
sverja (svarð-) *vb* swear
svipta (-pt-) *vb* [*w dat*] sweep, pull quickly
Svíakonungr *m* king of the Swedes
Svíar *m pl* Swedes
Svíþjóð *f* Sweden
svíkja (svíkr; sveik, sviku; svikinn) *vb* betray
svǫrt *adj*, *see* **svartr**
syngja (syngr; sǫng, sungu; sunginn) *vb* sing
syni, **synir** *m*, *see* **sonr**
synja (-að-) *vb* [*w gen*] refuse, deny
systir (*acc/dat/gen* systur; *pl* systr, *dat* systrum, *gen* systra) *f* sister
sýn (*pl* -ir) *f* sign, vision, appearance; **ólíkr sýnum** different in appearance; **fegri sýnum** more beautiful (in appearance)
sýna (-d-) *vb* show; *refl* **sýnask** [*w dat*] appear, seem (*impers*); **sýnisk mér** it seems to me
sæti *n* seat
sætt *f* settlement, agreement, reconciliation; **vera/verða at sætt** constitute a settlement or agreement
sættask (-tt-) *refl vb* become reconciled
sœkja (sótt-) *vb* seek; **sœkja sǫkum** prosecute
sœnskr *adj* Swedish
sǫgðu *vb*, *see* **segja**

sǫðull *m* saddle
sǫgu *f*, *see* **saga**
sǫk (*gen* sakar; *pl* sakar/sakir) *f* reason, cause, sake; prosecution, lawsuit; **sǫk til [e-s]** reason for [sth], cause of [sth]; **fyrir ... sakar** on account of, because of
sǫkkva (søkkr; sǫkk, sukku; sokkinn) *vb* sink

T

taka (tekr; tók, tóku; tekinn) *vb* take, catch, seize; reach, stretch forth, touch; receive (a person); begin; [*w inf*] begin to do; *refl* **takask** begin, happen; **taka af** take away, remove from; **taka á** touch; **taka hǫndum** take hold of, seize with the hands; **taka í sundr** cut in two; **taka til ráða** adopt a plan; **taka [e-m] vel** receive [sb] well; **taka við** receive; **taka undir sik** take charge of
tala (-að-) *vb* speak; **fegrst talaðr** most eloquent
Tálknafjǫrðr *m* name of a fjord in NW Iceland
tekit *ppart*, *see* **taka**
temja (tamd-) *vb* tame
tiginn *adj* noble (of family)
tigr (*gen* -ar; *pl nom* -ir, *acc* -u) *m* ten, group of ten; **sex tigir** *num* [*w gen*] sixty; **sjau tigir** *num* [*w gen*] seventy; **þrír tigir** *num* [*w gen*] thirty
til *prep* [*w gen*] to, until; for; with respect to, for the sake of; **til þess** the reason for this; **til þess at** to, in order to; **til þess er** until; **búask til** prepare for; **gera brúðlaup til** marry; **jafna til** compare with; **sem hon átti ætt til** which was characteristic for her family
til *adv* **vera til** to exist, be at hand; **bœta til um** improve; **ganga til** approach, go up to a thing; **leggja til (orð)** say
tíðendi *n pl* news, tidings; **er þetta var tíðenda** when this happened
tími *m* time; **þenna tíma** at this time; **í þann tíma** at that time
tíu *num* ten
topt *n* toft, site of a house; foundation or bare walls, ruins of a house
Toptavǫllr *m* Toptavoll ('Field of Ruined Walls') (*place name*)
tók, **tóksk**, **tóku** *vb*, *see* **taka**
tólf *num* twelve
trúa (-ð-) *vb* [*w dat*] trust
Tryggvi *m* Tryggvi (*personal name*)
tunga *f* tongue
tuttugu *num* twenty
tveir (*f* tvær, *n* tvau; *acc m* tvá, *all dat* tveim(r), *all gen* tveggja) *num* two
tylft (*pl* -ir) *f* dozen, group of twelve; a half day's sail
tæla (-d-) *vb* betray; entice, entrap
tœki *vb*, *see* **taka**

U

ull (*dat* ullu) *f* wool
ullarlagðr *m* tuft of wool
um *prep* [*w acc*] around, about, in regard to; during, in (*time*); **um alla hluti** in all respects; **um fram** in addition; **um várit** in the spring; **bœta til um** improve
umhverfis *adv* around, round about
undan *adv* away; **biðjask undan** be evasive; **komask undan** escape
undir *prep* [*w acc/dat*] under
ungmenni *n* young people, children
ungr *adj* young; **á ungum aldri** young
unna (ann, unnu; unni; unn(a)t) *vb* [*w dat of person*, *gen of thing*] grant, allow; [*w dat*] love
upp *adv* up (*motion*), upwards; **upp með** up along; **koma upp** come about, happen
Uppsalir *m pl* Uppsala ('Upper Halls'), a town in Sweden (*place name*)
Urðarbrunnr *m* 'Urd's Well' (*place name*)
urðarmaðr *m* outlaw; **gera at urðarmanni** to outlaw
Urðr *f* Urd ('Fate'), one of the Norns (*see* **verða**)
urðu *vb*, *see* **verða**

Ú

ú- *pref, see* **ó-**
úlfr *m* wolf
úr *prep, see* **ór**
út *adv* out (*motion*), outwards
útan *adv* from without, from outside; **fyrir útan** [*w acc*] outside; out beyond
úti *adv* outside (*location*)
útlenzkr *adj* foreign
útsjár *m* ocean

V

Valaskjálf *f* 'Vali's Seat' (*place name*)
valda (veldr; olli, ollu; valdit) *vb* [*w dat*] wield, control, rule over; cause
valði *vb, see* **velja**
vandliga *adv* carefully
vandræði *n pl* trouble, difficulty
var *vb, see* **vera**
varð *vb, see* **verða**
vara (-ð-; *ppart* varat) *vb* give (one) a foreboding of; **þat varir [e-n]** [sb] has a presentiment
varr *adj* aware; **verðr [e-m] varr við [e-t]** [sb] becomes aware of [sth]
vaskligr *adj* brave, bold
vaskr *adj* brave, valiant
vatn (*pl* vǫtn) *n* water
vágr *m* bay
vágskorinn *adj* scored with bays
ván (*pl* -ir) *f* hope; expectation, prospect
vándr (*n* vánt) *adj* bad, wretched
vápn *n* weapon; **bera vápn á [e-n]** raise a weapon against [sb]
Vápnafjǫrðr *m* Vápnafjord ('Weapon's Fjord') (*place name*)
vár *n* spring; **um várit** in the spring
vár *pron, see* **vér**
várr *poss adj* our
váru *vb, see* **vera**
veggr (*gen* -jar/s; *pl* -ir) *m* wall
vegr *m* way, path, road
veiða (-dd-) *vb* catch; hunt
veiðr (*acc/dat* veiði, *gen* veiðar; *pl* veiðar) *f* catch
veikr *adj* weak
veit *vb, see* **vita**
veitt *ppart, see* **veiða**
veizla *f* feast, party
vekja (vakt-) *vb* wake
vel (*comp* betr, *superl* bezt) *adv* well, very, very much; **vel viti borinn** intelligent, endowed with good sense
veld *vb, see* **valda**
velja (valð-) *vb* choose, select
venja (vanð-/vand-) *vb* accustom, train
vera (er; var, váru; verit) *vb* be; **vera nǫkkut við** be somehow connected with; **vera til** exist, be at hand; **er/var [e-m] [e-t]** [sb] has/had [sth]; **[e-t] er/var at** it is/was [sth]
verða (verðr; varð, urðu; orðinn) *vb* become; happen, come to pass; **verða af** come about, appear; **verða at** [*w inf*] must, need to, be obliged to [do sth]; **verða [e-m] at meini** cause [sb] harm; **verða varr við [e-t]** become aware of [sth]; **eigi mun svá mikill brestr orðinn** such a great break is not likely to have occurred
Verðandi *f* Verdandi ('Becoming', *pres part of* **verða**), one of the Norns
verit *ppart, see* **vera**
verr *comp adv* worse (*see* **illa**)
verri *comp adj* worse (*see* **illr**)
verst *superl adv* worst (*see* **illa**)
verstr *superl adj* worst (*see* **illr**)
vestr *n* the west; *adv* west, westwards; **í vestr** west(wards)
vetr (*gen* vetrar; *pl* vetr) *m* winter; year (*in reckoning time*); **um vetrinn** during the winter
Vé *m* Ve, brother of Odin (*mythological name*)
vér (*acc/dat* oss, *gen* vár) *pron* we (*pl*)
Vésteinn *m* Vestein (*personal name*)
við *prep* [*w acc*] with, to; at, by, close to; according to, after; **lifa við** live on, feed on; **mæla við** say to, speak to; **taka við** receive; **vera nǫkkut við** be somehow connected with
viðr (*dat* við(i)) *m* tree

vilja (vill; vildi; viljat; *pret inf* vildu) *vb* want, wish, will
vinátta *f* friendship
vinna (vinnr; vann, unnu; unninn) *vb* gain, win; overcome, conquer; work, perform, do; till, cultivate (land); **vinna at [e-m]** do away with, kill [sb]
vinr (*gen* -ar; *pl* -ir) *m* friend
vinsæll *adj* popular, blessed with friends
virðask (-rð-) *refl vb* [*w dat*] seem, think (*impers*); **mér virðisk** it seems to me
vissi, **vissu** *vb*, *see* **vita**
vist (*gen* -ar; *pl* -ir) *f* food, provisions
vit (*acc/dat* okkr, *gen* okkar) *pron* we (two)
vit *n* good sense, wit, intelligence; **vel viti borinn** intelligent, endowed with good sense
vita (veit, vitu; vissi; vitaðr) *vb* know
vitja (-að-) *vb* [*w gen*] visit
vitr (*gen* vitrs) *adj* wise
vígja (-ð-) *vb* ordain, consecrate
víking *f* sea-raiding; **vera í víking** be engaged in sea-raiding
víkingr *m* a viking, sea-raider
Vílir *m* Vili, brother of Odin (*mythological name*)
vísa *f* verse
víss *adj* certain, sure
vænn *adj* fine, handsome, beautiful
væri *vb*, *see* **vera**
vættr (*dat* vætti, *gen* vættar, *pl* vættir) *f* creature, being; **ekki vætta** nothing at all
vǫllr (*dat* velli, *gen* vallar; *pl* vellir, *acc* vǫllu, *gen* valla) *m* field
Vǫlsungr *m* Volsung (*personal name*); father of Sigmund
vǫxtr (*dat* vexti, *gen* vaxtar; *pl* vextir, *acc* vǫxtu, *gen* vaxta) *m* size, stature; **mikill vexti** big, great in stature

Y

yðar *pron*, *see* **þér**
yðarr *poss adj* your (*pl*)
yðr *pron*, *see* **þér**
yfir *prep* [*w acc/dat*] over, above; **konungr yfir** king of
yfirkonungr *m* supreme king
yfirlit *n* look, personal appearance
yfirmaðr *m* leader, chieftain
Yggdrasill *m* the tree of life
Ymir *m* Ymir, the first giant (*mythological name*)
Ynglingar *m pl* line of early Swedish kings
Yngvarr *m* Yngvar (*personal name*)
yrði *vb*, *see* **verða**
yztr *superl adj* outermost (*compare* **út**)

Þ

þaðan *adv* from there, thence
þak *n* roof
þagði *vb*, *see* **þegja**
þangat *adv* (to) there, thither; **þangat til** to there
þann *dem pron/adj*, *see* **sá**
þar *adv* there; **þar eptir** thereafter, accordingly; **þar sem** there where
þat (*dat* því, *gen* þess; *pl* þau) *pron* (*n*) it
þat (*dat* því, *gen* þess; *pl* þau) *dem pron/adj* (*n*) that (one) (*see* **sá**)
þau (*dat* þeim, *gen* þeira) *pron* they (*n and mixed*)
þau (*dat* þeim, *gen* þeira) *dem pron/adj* those (*n*) (*see* **þat** *and* **þeir**)
þá *pron*, *see* **þeir**
þá *dem pron/adj*, *see* **sú** *and* **þeir**
þá *adv* then; **þá er** *conj* when
þáttr (*dat* þætti) *m* short story, tale
þegar *adv* at once, immediately; *conj* as soon as
þegja (þagð-; *ppart* þagat) *vb* be silent; **þegja við** remain silent
þegnskapr (*gen* -ar) *m* generosity, open-handedness
þeim *pron*, *see* **þeir**
þeim *dem pron/adj*, *see* **sá** *and* **þeir**
þeir (*f* þær, *n* þau; *acc* þá, *dat* þeim, *gen* þeira) *pron* they (*m*)
þeir (*f* þær, *n* þau; *acc* þá, *dat* þeim, *gen* þeira) *dem pron/adj* those (*m*) (*see* **sá**)
þeira *pron*, *see* **þeir**

þeira *poss pron* their, theirs
þeira *dem pron/adj, see* **þeir**
þeirar, **þeiri** *dem pron/adj, see* **sú**
þekja (þakð-) *vb* cover, thatch
þenna *dem pron/adj, see* **þessi**
þess *dem pron/adj, see* **sá** *and* **þat**
þessi (*f* þessi, *n* þetta) *dem pron/adj* this (one); **þenna tíma** at this time
þetta *dem pron/adj, see* **þessi**
þér (*acc/dat* yðr, *gen* yð(v)ar) *pron* you (*pl*)
þér *pron, see* **þú**
þiggja (þiggr; þá, þágu; þeginn) *vb* accept
þik *pron, see* **þú**
þing *n* assembly
þingbrekka *f* slope on which assembly meetings were held
þingheimr *m* the attendance (those in attendance) at a **þing**
þinn (*f* þín, *n* þitt; *acc m* þinn, *f* þína, *dat m* þínum, *n* þínu, *gen m/n* þíns; *pl m* þínir, *f* þínar, *n* þín, *acc m* þína, *dat* þínum) *poss adj* your (*sg*)
þit (*acc/dat* ykkr, *gen* ykkar) *pron* we (two)
þín *pron, see* **þú**
Þjóð *f* Thjod ('People') (*place name*, modern province of Thy in Jutland, Denmark)
þola (-d-; *ppart* þol(a)t) *vb* suffer, endure
þora (-ð-) *vb* dare, have courage
Þorgeirr *m* Thorgeir (*personal name*)
Þorgerðr *f* Thorgerd (*personal name*)
Þorgils *m* Thorgils (*personal name*)
Þorgrímr *m* Thorgrim (*personal name*)
Þorkell *m* Thorkel (*personal name*)
Þormóðr *m* Thormod (*personal name*)
þorp *n* village, hamlet
Þorsteinn *m* Thorstein (*personal name*)
þó *adv* yet, though, nevertheless
Þóra *f* Thora (*personal name*)
Þórarinn *m* Thorarin (*personal name*)
Þórbjǫrn *m* Thorbjorn (*personal name*)
Þórdís *f* Thordis (*personal name*)
Þórðr *m* Thord (*personal name*)
Þórir *m* Thorir (*personal name*)
Þórólfr *m* Thorolf (*personal name*)
þótt (= **þó at**) *conj* [*w subjunct*] although, even though
þótti, **þóttu** *vb, see* **þykkja**
þrettán *num* thirteen
þriði *ord num* third
þrír (*f* þrjár, *n* þrjú; *acc m* þrjá, *all dat* þrim(r)/þrem(r), *all gen* þriggja) *num* three; **þrír tigir** *num* [*w gen*] thirty
þrǫngr *adj* narrow
þurfa (þarf, þurfu; þurfti; þurft) *vb* [*w gen*] need, have need of
þú (acc þik, *dat* þér, *gen* þín) *pron* you (*sg*); **ór hendi þér** out of your hands
því *pron, see* **þat**
því *dem pron/adj, see* **þat**
því *conj* because (*n dat of* **þat**); **(fyrir) því at** because
þykkja (þótt-) *vb* [*w dat*] seem (*impers*); **Ásum þótti ørvænt hans heim** the gods gave up hope of his returning home; **okkrum mundi þykkja** it would seem to us; *refl* **þykkjask** seem to one, consider oneself; **þykkjask vita** feel convinced
þyldi *vb, see* **þola**
þysja (þust-) *vb* rush
þær (*dat* þeim, *gen* þeira) *pron* they (*f*)
þær (*dat* þeim, *gen* þeira) *dem pron/adj* those (*f*) (*see* **sú** *and* **þeir**)
þœtti *vb, see* **þykkja**
þǫkðu *vb, see* **þekja**

Æ

Æsa *f* Æsa (*personal name*)
Æsir *pl of* **Áss**
æti *vb, see* **eta**
ætla (-að-) *vb* think, intend; agree
ætt (*pl* -ir) *f* family; **sem hon átti ætt til** which was characteristic for her family
ætti *vb, see* **eiga**
ævi *f* time, lifetime, age

Œ

œðri *comp adj* higher
œgir (*gen* -is) *m* one who frightens
œgishjálmr *m* helmet of dread
œrinn *adj* sufficient, enough
œska *f* youth, childhood
œxla (-t-) *vb* multiply, increase

Ǫ

ǫðru, **ǫðrum** *adj*, *see* **annarr**
ǫflugr *adj* strong, powerful
ǫld (*gen* aldar; *pl* aldir) *f* age
ǫll, **ǫllu**, **ǫllum** *adj*, *see* **allr**
Ǫlvir *m* Olvir (*personal name*)
ǫnnur *adj*, *see* **annarr**
Ǫnundr *m* Onund (*personal name*)
ǫr (-v-) *f* arrow
ǫrn (*dat* erni, *gen* arnar; *pl* ernir, *acc* ǫrnu, *gen* arna) *m* eagle
ørvænt *adj* past hope; **Ásum þótti ørvænt hans heim** the gods gave up hope of his returning home
øxn *m*, *see* **oxi**
Øxna-Þórir *m* Thorir 'of the Oxen' (*personal name*)

FURTHER SUGGESTED READINGS
OLD NORSE - OLD ICELANDIC LANGUAGE, RUNES, SOCIETY, AND CULTURE...

THE VIKING LANGUAGE SERIES

A modern introduction to Old Norse language, runes, Icelandic sagas, Viking history and literature. Perfect for the modern classroom, online teaching, and the self-learner.

Viking Language 1: Learn Old Norse, Runes and Icelandic Sagas (2nd Edition) is a new introduction to Old Norse, Icelandic sagas, and runes. Everything from beginner to advanced in one book: graded lessons, vocabulary, grammar exercises, pronunciation, and extensive maps. Includes sections on Viking history, literature, and myth. Innovative word-frequency method greatly speeds learning and Modern Icelandic has changed little from Old Norse; students are well on the way to mastering Modern Icelandic. EBOOK AVAILABLE.

Viking Language 2: The Old Norse Reader is a treasure trove of Scandinavian lore, immersing the learner in a wide variety of Old Norse sources and runes. *The Reader* offers a large vocabulary, chapters on Eddic and skaldic poetry, and a full reference grammar: the latter can be invaluable while learning to read sagas. It includes complete sagas, runic inscriptions, myths, creation stories, legends, with Eddic poems about Scandinavian gods, monster-slayers, dwarves, giants, and warrior kings and Valkyries.

PRONUNCIATION ALBUMS

Audio Lessons 1-8, Audio Lessons 9-15

Two MP3 albums teach the pronunciation of saga passages and runes in *Viking Language 1*. The pronunciation is a slightly archaic Modern Icelandic as used in the saga and language courses at the University of Iceland. Both albums are available on Amazon and iTunes for download and purchase. **Check out free sample lessons at oldnorse.org.**

FURTHER OLD NORSE RESOURCES FROM JULES WILLIAM PRESS...

Old Norse–Old Icelandic: Concise Introduction to the Language of the Sagas answers the need for a modern method to learn the language of the sagas. This new primer requires no previous language knowledge, and the beginner quickly starts reading original passages from Icelandic sagas, mythological texts, and sources about the Viking Age. Designed for quick learning on one's own or in class, the lessons supply all necessary grammar, exercises, and vocabulary.

Supplementary Exercises for Old Norse - Old Icelandic complements *Old Norse-Old Icelandic: Concise Introduction to the Language of the Sagas* by providing additional exercises and vocabulary activties. Together, these two books make the sagas accessible for anyone learning Old Norse and the Viking Age.

AUCH IN DEUTSCH ERHÄLTLICH

(Also Available in German)

***Altnordisch 1: Die Sprache der Wikinger, Runen und isländischen Saga**s* gliedert sich in fünfzehn inhaltlich aufeinander aufbauende Lektionen bestehend aus altnordischen Textpassagen, Runen, Grammatikbaukästen, Übungen, Karten. Das Buch enthält ein vollständiges Wörterverzeichnis, eine Kurzgrammatik sowie Hinweise zur (rekonstruierten) Aussprache.

The Viking Language Series is available as paperbacks and ebooks on Amazon (UK, US, DE, FR, IT, ES, JP, CA) and for booksellers on Ingram.

Free Answer Key and Audio Pronunciation Samples: www.oldnorse.org.

COMING SOON FROM JWP...

THE ICELANDIC SAGA SERIES

Our Icelandic Saga series includes new English translations together with the original Old Norse, as well as introductions, vocabulary, grammar, maps and notes.

The Tale of Thorstein Staff Struck (Þorsteins þáttr stangarhöggs) is a short saga set in Iceland's East Fjords during the 10th-century Viking Age. Thorstein, a peaceful young man, is forced to live with the humiliating nickname "staff struck." Even Thorstein's father, an old Viking, looks down on his son as a coward. But Thorstein is no coward. Waiting for the right moment to take revenge, Thorstein reclaims his good name in a way that brings honor both to him and his chieftain.

The Saga of the Families of Weapon's Fjord (Vápnfirðinga saga) is a classic Icelandic saga of feuding chieftains and their families struggling for power and survival. Set during the 10th-century Viking Age in Iceland's East Fjords, the saga recounts how a rich Norwegian merchant stirs the greed of the local inhabitants. Sons avenge fathers, while wives and mothers demand honor for their families. In this new edition, a world in the far North Atlantic opens for the modern reader.

Egil's Bones: Icelandic Sagas, Blood Feud, and Viking Archaeology (The Writings of Jesse Byock) explores Viking Age Iceland — its origins, sagas, heroes, society, and archaeology. The studies provide a comprehensive picture of this North Atlantic island founded more than 1,000 years ago. The pages explore the background of legendary heroes such as the Viking warrior poet, Egil Skalla-Grimsson and his archaeological bones as well as Sigurd the dragon slayer, whose saga influenced J.R.R. Tolkien and Richard Wagner's Ring Cycle.

OTHER WORKS BY JESSE BYOCK

Viking Age Iceland combines anthropology, archaeology, and history offering crucial insights into the Icelandic sagas and the inner workings of a feuding society with intriguing proto-democratic tendencies. Unusual for Western Europe, Iceland had no king, no foreign policy, no defence forces, and no great lords. It should have been a utopia, yet its sagas are dominated by blood feud and killings. Reasons for this, argues Jesse Byock, lie in the cultural codes and processes of conflict within the island's social order and the Viking world.

Feud in the Icelandic Saga explores conflicts at the core of the Old Icelandic sagas. Jesse Byock shows how the dominant concern of medieval Icelandic society was the channeling of violence into accepted patterns of feud and the regulation of conflict, processes that are reflected in the family and the *Sturlunga* sagas. This comprehensive study of narrative structure and the control of violence explores the sagas as revealing expressions of medieval social thought.

Made in the USA
Middletown, DE
20 June 2022

67450970R10068